JAPANESE FOLK TALES

A Revised Selection

JAPANESE FOLK TALES

A Revised Selection
By KUNIO YANAGITA

❖

Translated by FANNY HAGIN MAYER

❖

Illustrated by KEI WAKANA

❖

TOKYO NEWS SERVICE, LTD.

Published 1966

●

All rights reserved

●

This is a translation of Kunio Yanagita, *Nippon no*
Mukashibanashi Kaitei Han,
Tokyo: Kadokawa, 1960

Library of Congress Catalog Card Number: 66-18704

Published and printed by

TOKYO NEWS SERVICE, LTD.

10, Ginza Nishi 8-chome,
Chuo-ku, Tokyo, Japan

CONTENTS

Translator's Introduction

The tales:

5

TRANSLATOR'S INTRODUCTION

Mr. Yanagita kindly wrote an Introduction for readers of my English translation of his earlier collection of Japanese folk tales.* Since he is no longer here to do the same for his revised selection, I shall undertake it. I have translated his Introduction to the Japanese edition and its Postscript, written by Hisako Maruyama and Yasuyo Ishiwara, and included them at the end of this book. Written at the age of eighty-five, Yanagita's Introduction shows his devotion to the very last to the task of recording the folk tales of his country and to making them known.

The general reader will find in this revised selection a number of newly translated tales from the great number orally transmitted and recently recorded. In the earlier edition there were 108 tales, but forty-five of them were legends or popular fiction. These have been replaced in the present volume by forty-three genuine folk tales.

The student of Japanese folk tales will find the present collection of value because of its clearly indicated sources of the references. Author and title for those that are books, volume and number of journals, and collector's names whose manuscripts have been used. The old geographical names of the earlier text have been replaced by modern place names. The Distribution Map will help this information to be of further use. The translator has added a Reference Index and Geographical Index, hoping they will be helpful.

In the Postscript there is an explanation of the basis for selecting the tales. To the aims, a widely scattered geographical representation and suitability, there might well have been added a third, for the selections mark the progress in gathering tales and

---

* Translation of *Nippon no Mukashibanashi* (Japanese Folk Tales) appeared in *Folklore Studies*, Vol. XI, No. 2 (1952); a revised version, Tokyo News Service, 1954, both by the present translator.

recording them in Japan from 1910 to the present. I will comment a little further upon these to guide those who may want more information about them, particularly the last named matter.

In examining the geographical distribution of these tales, one must keep in mind that it was made with Japanese readers in mind. Recording tales in Japan has centered around local regions for the most part. There have been a few exceptions. *Nippon Zenkoku Kokumin Dōwa (10)** by Kendō Ishii, *Nippon Densetsu Shū (46)* by Toshio Takagi, the earlier work by Yanagita and his present collection, and *Nippon no Mukashibanashi* (Folk Tales of Japan), 3 Vols. (Tokyo, 1956-57) by Keigo Seki are all-Japan in scope. Most readers, however, want to see their own local tales in a collection. In that sense this book has satisfied many to the extent it has tales from thirty-three of the forty-five prefectures in Japan, not counting Hokkaidō.

Some foreign readers may be interested in the geographical distribution of individual tales, but that was not in the mind of Yanagita in making the choice. Information about single tales can be found in *Nippon Mukashibanashi Meii* (A Classification of Japanese Folk Tales) by Yanagita, 1948, or *Nippon Mukashibanashi Shūsei* (A Compilation of Japanese Folk Tales), 3 Parts (6 Vols.) by Seki, 1950-58.

The aim of suitability needs some explanation. That it was determined with "young people" in mind in no way implies that the choice is other than a genuine folk tale. The principal interest in many versions of a tale is its dialect. Local dialects are mostly unintelligible to Japanese at large. While collectors have their reasons for recording tales in dialect, the general reader, especially that of the younger generation, can put up with only a certain amount of it. He wants to read for the story, not to study dialect. The tales here have clear plots and the dialect has been modified to where the vocabulary is understandable. A few tales have been rendered into modern Japanese from old literary records or local records. Such changes do not concern translations. I have examined most of the original sources of this collection and can state that

---

* Numbers in parenthesis following titles refer to the Reference Index. Translation of titles and other information about publication is also given there.

with few exceptions the story itself has not been modified. Where it was, it was usually to give a fuller version of what was a bare outline. In other words, the tales in this book are from standard sources and not rewritten for children.

Recognizing the need for rewritten versions, an editorial committee of specialists in juvenile literature and the folk tale, Jōji Tsubota, Hirosuke Hamada, Tokihiko Oto, and Hisako Maruyama, with the advice of Yanagita, published a series called *Nippon no Mukashibanashi,* Student Edition, (1956-57), one volume for each of the six elementary grades. These tales were rewritten and signed by various writers who could adapt them to the reading levels of children. At the end of each volume was a section which gave the exact source and some commentary for each tale. A total of 109 authentic folk tales were thus put into the hands of children in a form they could read themselves. It should be clear that Yanagita did not intend to give what is usually considered a book of the juvenile category in his Kadokawa edition.

There remains the significance of the sources of the present edition to be discussed. The Reference Index will yield something of the chronology for them but not throw light upon their significance. Although not one of the stated aims of the book, the references, nevertheless, are representative of a large body of material not included. They also give a story of the search for folk tales from the beginning of the movement to the present. In fact, Collector Sato's tale, No. 52, is now to be found in his *Fukuoka no Mukashibanashi* (Folk Tales from Fukuoka), 1963.

Mr. Yanagita has said in his Introduction that a long introduction to a small book is a joke. Then I will join him in his little joke by matching his with a long one of my own. The story of the work of Japanese collectors has not been told abroad yet. For those who would like some light upon the subject, I will offer comments on the sources of this book from that point of view. From 1910 to 1960 makes an even five decades into which I will divide the references. References in Yanagita's book come from a variety of sources — old literary works, local records, journals, and collections of tales. I shall touch upon these in the various periods.

The year 1910 marks the real beginning, albeit a chance one, for collecting folk tales in Japan. It was in that year that Yanagita published his *Tōno Monogatari* (Tōno Tales), a record of local customs, traditions, and lore of Tōno district in Iwate prefecture as recounted by Kizen Sasaki, a young man who lived there. Yanagita wrote later that it was not until he had returned to Tokyo that it dawned upon him that he had in his notes two genuine folk tales of the kind folklorists in England and Europe were studying. Here in Japan were undoubtedly countless more for the searching and he lost no time starting and enlisting others in the task.

The reason for including literary sources such as *Shaseki-shū (39), Seisuisho (38),* and *Kaidōki (17)* is given in the Postscript. An old local record, *Kazunoshi (20),* compiled in 1877, furnishes one source. The *Riyō Shū (35),* gathered under the direction of the Ministry of Education in 1914, shows that the newly aroused interest was echoed in high places. The journal *Kyōdo Kenkyū (22),* initiated by Yanagita and Takagi in 1913, attracted attention all over Japan, furnishing a forum for exchanging findings and ideas. Volume I to IV appeared from 1913 to 1917 and Volume V to VII from 1931 to 1934.

Ishii and Takagi have already been mentioned as individuals who produced all-Japan collections. Their work was a direct response to Yanagita's happy discovery. Ishii sent letters all over the country and went in person when possible to collect tales. Looking back upon his choices from the present point of progress, students may feel that some of them are not of much value and his geographical distribution of them can be questioned in several instances. But his was a brave start under a title that made a good rallying call. Takagi took more time. For six months, from the end of May, 1911, he ran an ad in *Tokyo Asahi Shimbun,* asking for local legends and stories to be sent in. He spent the next year and a half selecting and editing contributions for his work, which remains of value to this day.

Two other works of individuals furnish sources from this early decade. *Nansō no Rizoku (48)* records village lore and *Kii Arita-gun Dōwa Shū (29)* gives a collection of local stories for children.

Local records compiled in offices of *gun* or village that contained tales in the second decade have been tapped. These are *Azuma-gun Shi (1), Chichibu Tsukikawa Sonshi (2), Ishikawa-ken Kashima-gun Shi (11), Minamiazumi-gun Shi (24),* and *Uzen Toyo-*

sato Sonshi (50). After the war that kind of writing was often turned over to outside specialists, the contents becoming standardized and less colorful.

The second decade saw two more journals of interest to folklore, which furnish some of the references. *Minzoku (26)*, directed by Chikai Okumura from 1925 to 1929 and *Tabi to Densetsu (45)*, directed by Masanori Hagiwara, began in 1928 and continued through 1944. These were leavening agents for interest in folklore and often contained local tales from which Yanagita has made selections.

A local effort of another kind selected in this second decade was *Impaku Dōwa (8)*, one of a series of little publications of a local group in Tottori which was interested in local history, legends, and tales.

The publishing firm Kyōdo Kenkyū-sha began a major project in this decade. Its Rōhen Sōsho (Hearth-side Series) covered folkore from Hokkaidō in the north to the Mariana Islands in the south. I have thirty-six of the series. These are little books from a little over one hundred to more than two hundred pages. So far as I can see, each author wrote and signed his introduction. The earliest that I have came out in 1920 and the latest in 1929. I also have a little 24-page booklet written in 1925 for the Series by Yanagita in which he offered a one-page description for each of twenty of the books, by which he hoped to draw out more contributions.

Sasaki, who had given up his studies in literature at Waseda University, due to ill health, followed his contribution to Yanagita's *Tōno Monogatari* with numerous articles to journals and newspapers from 1912 to 1933, the year of his death. Of his six collections of folk tales, three were published in the Rōhen Series. One of these, *Esashi-gun Mukashibanashi (36)*, gives three tales to this collection. Another Rōhen book, *Echigo Sanjō Nangō Dan (41)*, also supplies three.

Besides Sasaki's Rōhen collections, his *Rōō Yatan (37)* also is used as a source. Two other works of individual authors in this second decade are *Izawa-gun Mukashibanashi Shū (34)* and *Tsugaru Kōhi Shū (49)*.

In the '30s the total volume of collections soared. Locally

issued studies are represented by *Fukui-ken Kyōdo Shi (5),* published as Vol. 2 of popular oral traditions collected by high school students. Other local efforts are represented by two normal schools. These two, *Shizuoka-ken Densetsu Mukashibanashi Shū (40)* and *Geibi Sōsho Mukashibanashi Kenkyū (7),* were compiled at their study centers. The contents of these school collections vary in length from brief field notes to full length folk tales. They are, however, valuable regional sources.

Mikan Denshō (25), a journal begun in 1935, continues to this day. It started under the direction of Tarō Wakamori. Yanagita has discussed his *Mukashibanashi Kenkyū (30)* in his Introduction. His comments about that and *Saishū Techō* are understatements. *Mukashibanashi Kenkyū* was issued only from 1935 to 1937, but it is indispensible to a student of Japanese folk tales and *Saishū Techō* became the basis for designating titles and arranging tales in many later collections.

The great number of collections of tales in the third decade is well represented by the choices made for Yanagita's collection. *Kai Mukshibanashi Shū (3), Zoku Kai Mukashibanashi Shū (zoku* meaning additional) *(4), Akinokuni Mukashibanashi Shū (12), Ikinoshima Mukashibanashi Shū (51), Kawagoe Chihō Mukashibanashi Shū (43),* and *Shinano Mukashibanashi Shū (23)* are selections distributed from Nagano south to Nagasaki. A selection has been taken from Fukuoka Prefecture as recorded in a manuscript whose origin is not clear.

No local records or journals seem to have made their start in the fourth decade, which was one of great difficulty due to the war. With interest in the folk tales rising to a high point by the end of the 30's and from the great volume of material in hand, Yanagita expected in the following decade to put out a series of volumes representative of various regions in what he called the Zenkoku Kiroku (All-Japan Series). What he began in 1942 had to be given up by March of 1944. Thirteen books had come out by then. Sources selected from these are from *Iwaki Mukashibanashi Shū (16), Kikaijima Mukashibanashi Shū (13), Koshikijima Mukashibanashi Shū (14), Naori-gun Mukashibanashi Shū (42),* and *Sanuki Sanagi-shishijima Mukashibanashi Shū (47).*

Other than the Zenkoku Kiroku, collections or studies by individuals furnish some sources. Before the close of the war there are works on folklore such as *Akita Gunyū Gyotan (31)*, *Ōsumi Kimotsuki-gun Hōgen Shū (33)*, and *Yoshino Saiō Minzoku Saihōki (27)*. After the close of the war two collections of folk tales by individuals have furnished selections. These are *Ninohe Mukashibanashi Shū (21)* and *Tosa Mukashibanashi Shū (19)*.

Although local records were complied in the days that brought security to the land, I have explained why these have not been used. One reference, however, is from a village record in this fifth and last decade. It is from *Iōjima-mura Kyōdo Shi (9)*. A local journal, *Kano Minzoku (18)*, also furnishes one tale.

There are old names among individual collectors. Tōzō Suzuki, who collected the Kawagoe tales and contributed one volume to the Zenkoku Kiroku, brought out *Kuttan Jijii no Hanashi (44)*; Ichirō Iwaurka, who furnished three of the Zenkoku Kiroku, published *Okinoerabu Mukashibanashi (15)*; and Tayako Noda, a veteran folklorist, published her first collection of tales, *Tekkiri Anesama (32)*, stories she had heard as a girl in Aomori. The new name is that of Kenichi Mizusawa. He has published eight volumes of folk tales since 1956, and as this Introduction is being written, word comes from him that two more will soon appear. Two tales from his *Tonto Mukashi Ga Atta Gedo, Dai Isshū* (Vol. I) *(28)* are in Yanagita's book.

I would like to introduce the collectors whose manuscripts have furnished sources. Mrs. Sumako Osada has a valuable fund of lore about her native Amami Ōshima. Yoshihiro Sato and Takiko Sugawara are young people in Iwate. Sato's collection is now in book form and Miss Sugawara, now married, continues her interest in the folk tale. Dr. Hiroko Ikeda's research in folk tales earned her a doctorate at Indiana University. Hisako Maruyama, one of the assistants of Yanagita in revising his collection, always prefers to remain in the background. She is, nevertheless, one of the best versed in folk tales in Japan.

Even brief comments upon sources represented in Yanagita's book have lengthened this Introduction considerably. Since there is no book in English about the Japanese folk tale, information must be picked up from various sources. Yanagita's collection was written for the general reader, but it is of value to the student. Whether examined for motifs or thought patterns, the tales in it are of interest. As a book written by a Japanese scholar for his general reader, it is also of interest. The translator shares with a number of Japanese scholars the view that it is too soon to set up a fixed index to the tales. Collecting is still going on and among those already collected there are big problems involving variatons and sources. A comparative study of oriental tales, when that becomes really possible, offers a far more significant prospect for a basis of indexing, much more so than trying to fit single tales into a western index.

I wish I could conclude with suggestions for further reading in translation. Many genuine folk tales were included in Fritz Rumpf, *Japanese Volksmärchen* (Jena, 1938) and the newly published Fritz Briebüsse, *Volkserzählungen* (Asian Folklore Studies, Monograph No. 3, Tokyo, 1965). Besides these in German there are English editions, the earlier translation from Yanagita and the present revised selection, and selections from Seki's *Nippon no Mukashibanashi* translated by Robert Adams, *Folk Tales of Japan* (Chicago University Press, 1963). Since Adams included oral versions of tales already introduced by Mitford, Griffis, Chamberlain, Hearne, and others, as well as some already translated from Yanagita, the number of new tales in his work is less than forty. Between us we have made a beginning in English translations.

I am obliged to Miss Maruyama and Miss Ishiwara for help in problems of reading and translating in the new tales of this edition.

This collection, as has already been stated several times, was made primarily for the general reader and it is to him, therefore, I am especially happy to offer my translation.

Fanny Hagin Mayer
Sophia University

July 17, 1965

JAPANESE
FOLK
TALES

A Revised Selection

1. WHY THE MONKEY'S TAIL IS SHORT

Ages and ages ago the monkey's tail used to be thirty-three fathoms long. Because of a trick the bear played upon him, it turned into that short kind of a tail.

One time the monkey called at the bear's house and asked, "What is a good way to catch a lot of river fish?"

After talking it over, the bear advised, "On a cold night like this, sit on a rock above some deep place in the river and try putting that tail of yours down into the water and leaving it there. Many kinds of little fish will be sure to come and fasten onto it."

The monkey gladly did as he was told. As night deepened, his tail grew heavier and heavier. That was because the ice was spreading, but the monkey thought that the little fish were fastening onto his tail.

"This is enough to catch," he decided at last. "I want to go home because it is too cold."

He tried to pull up his tail, but no matter what he did, he could not get it loose. "This is awful," he cried, thrashing around. At last when he gave a desperate tug, his tail was snapped off at its base.

There are some people who say that the reason the monkey's face is so red is because he strained too hard as he pulled so frantically.

— Toshio Takagi, *Nippon Densetsu Shū*, p. 55*
(Matsue, Shimane)

---

* Page numbers have been added by the translator when possible.

2. WHY THE JELLYFISH HAS NO BONES

Long, long ago the consort of the king of the Dragon Palace was about to have a baby, and she had a strange craving to eat monkey liver. Wanting to satisfy her desire in some way or another, the Dragon King called for the turtle, one of his subjects, and asked him if he could think of a good way.

The turtle was a wise creature. He set out immediately and went across to the island of Japan. There he found a monkey playing in the mountain near the seashore.

"Master Monkey, Master Monkey, don't you feel like going to the Dragon Palace as a guest?" he asked. "There are big mountains there, too, and all kinds of feasts. If you go, I will give you a ride," he offered, displaying his big back.

The unsuspecting monkey was carried away by the fair words of the turtle and set out gaily to see the Dragon Palace. He found that it was indeed a far more splendid palace than what he had heard of.

While the monkey stood at the inner gate waiting for the turtle to come and guide him, the jellyfish, who was the gatekeeper, looked at the monkey's face and burst out laughing. "Master Monkey, you don't know a thing, do you?" he declared. "The royal consort is going to have a baby and she wants to eat monkey liver. That is why it happened that you were invited to come as a guest."

"This won't do," thought the startled monkey, but he was clever, too. He waited as if he didn't suspect a thing.

Presently the turtle came out and said, "Now, come this way."

"Master Turtle," exclaimed the monkey, "I have done something terribly foolish. If I had known it was going to be such weather as this, I would have brought my liver along, but I forgot and left it hanging out on a tree in the mountain to dry in the sun. If it starts to rain, it may get wet and I am worried."

"What, you came off and left your liver behind?" cried the turtle. "Then there is nothing to do but for you to go back and get it."

Thereupon he took the monkey onto his back once more and carried him back to the former shore. As soon as they reached the land, the monkey leaped away quickly and scrambled up to the top of the highest tree. Once there, he looked around as if nothing had happened.

In great alarm the turtle asked, "What is the matter, Monkey, old chap?"

With a laugh the monkey answered, "Inside the sea there can be no mountains; outside the body there can be no liver."

"That was surely because the loose-tongued jellyfish talked too much while the monkey was waiting at the gate," complained the turtle when he returned to the Dragon King.

"That unruly fellow!" shouted the king. "Peel all his scales off! Take all his bones out!"

That is why the jellyfish came to have the shape he has now. It was a punishment for his talking too much.

— *Shasekishū*, Maki 5, Part One, No. 8

3.   THE SPARROW AND THE WOODPECKER

Long, long ago the sparrow and the woodpecker were sisters. When a message came that their mother was sick and about to die, the sparrow was just blackening her teeth, but she flew quickly to her mother to take care of her. That is why even now her cheeks look soiled and the upper half of her beak is still white. The woodpecker, however, took her time, leisurely putting on rouge and powder and getting dressed up before she set out. Consequently she was too late to be there when her precious mother breathed her last.

That is why, although her appearance is not beautiful, the sparrow can always live where people are and eat as much as she needs of the grain people eat. Even though the woodpecker's face is beautifully made up, she can only fly around the woods

from early morning, hammering away, *gakka-mukka,* on the bark
of trees, barely finding three worms to eat in a day. When night
comes, she goes into the hollow of a tree and cries, *"Owae,
hashiga yameru deya* (Oh, my beak hurts)."

— Kunihiko Uchida, *Tsugaru Kōhi Shū,* p. 9
(Suehiro, Yoneda Koaza, Matsushima-mura, Tsugaru-gun, Aomori)

4. THE PIGEON'S OBEDIENCE TO HIS MOTHER

Long, long ago the pigeon was really a perverse fellow
who would not do a thing his mother wanted. If his mother
said to go to the mountains, he would go to the field. If his
mother said to go to the field, he would go to the garden to work.

His mother wanted to be buried on a quiet mountain-side
after she died, but she thought if she said so, her son would
do the opposite again, so she purposely asked him to make her
grave in the sand bar of the river.

Now it happened that after his mother died, the pigeon
realized for the first time how wrong it had been for him not to
have listened to what his mother said. This time he did just
as she had said and made her grave in the sand bar along the
river. When the river began to fill up with rain, however, the
pigeon became frantic for fear the grave would be washed away.

That is why even now, when it looks like rain, he recalls
this and cries, *"To-to-poppo, oya ga koishi (To-to-poppo,* I want
my mother)!"

It would have been better if he had obeyed his mother a
little sooner.

— *Kashima-gun Shi,* p. 980
(Kashima-gun, Ishikawa)

5. THE CUCKOO BROTHERS

Long, long ago the cuckoo had a very kind-hearted younger brother. Every year in May the younger brother would go to the mountains and dig lots of wild yams. He would cook them and give the very best ones to his elder brother to eat.

The elder brother distrusted him, in spite of that, and was sure that his brother saved the better yams to eat by himself. Finally, in a burst of hate, he brought a big butcher knife and killed his gentle little brother. He ripped open his stomach to see, but only coarse wild yams, full of holes, came out. Filled with remorse and grief over the terrible thing he had done, his form was changed into what it is now.

That is why even now, when the time comes to dig wild yams, the cuckoo flies around everywhere calling. If you listen well, he seems to cry,

> *Otōto koishi*
> *Hotte nite kuwaso*
> *Otōto koishi*
> *Imo hotte kuwaso.*
> (Little brother, I want you!
> I'd dig and cook and let you eat;
> Poor little brother,
> Yams I'd dig and let you eat.)

(Tōyama)

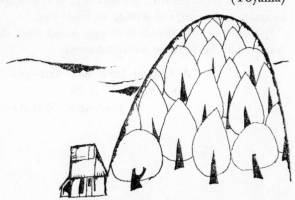

6.   THE CUCKOO AND THE SHRIKE

There is also a story how long, long ago the cuckoo was a shoemaker by trade. The shrike in those days was a packhorse leader. The shrike would always order the cuckoo to shoe his horse, but he never paid his bill.

The cuckoo remembered this and would forever call, *"Kutsu no dai wa doshita* (What about the shoe bill)?"

Then, because he was ashamed, the shrike would hide somewhere and not show his face when the time came for the cuckoo to come out and call. He would catch all kinds of little insects and fasten them onto twigs, leaving them to humor the cuckoo.

> — "A Legend from Kii, Naka-gun," *Kyōdo Kenkyū,*
>   Vol. IV, No. 7, p. 27
>   (Naka-gun, Wakayama)

However, there is also the following story, and it is hard to know which is true.

Long ago the shrike liked wine. The cuckoo left money with him with which he had agreed to buy an image of Buddha for his family altar, but he used all the money up on wine.

So the cuckoo is reminding the shrike when he comes around every year at that time and calls, *"Honzon kaketa ka* (Have you set up the image)?"

When he hears this, the shrike is so embarrassed that he keeps as quiet as he can, not daring to come out.

Some say that the shrike's face is red from drinking the wine, but it may be because he is ashamed.

> — "A Legend from Kii, Arita-gun," *Kyōdo Kenkyū,*
>   Vol. IV, No. 4, p. 26
>   (Arita-gun, Wakayama)

7.   THE LEGGING ON ONE LEG

Once upon a time there was a bird called Tokubo.   While he was eating some wheat that was good and ripe in the field one day, a husk got stuck in his throat and hurt him badly.   His friend who saw it happen rushed to tell Tokubo's mother.   The mother bird was putting on her leggings, getting ready to go off to work.   She was so flustered that she flew away just as she was with only one legging on.   In spite of her hurry, she did not reach her son in time.   He was dead by the time she got to him.

Ever since then when the wheat gets ripe, the mother bird flies around, yearning for her child and calling, "Tokubo, Tokubo!" It is said that even now feathers grow on only one leg of this bird.

— Geibi Mukashibanashi Kenkyū, p. 136
(Ōgaki-machi, Saheki-gun, Hiroshima)

8.   THE MEADOW LARK MONEY-LENDER

Long ago the meadow lark was a money-lender.   He loaned money to the sun, but it would never pay it back.   That is why when the meadow lark flies up into the sky, he calls, *"Zenzen kure, zen kure, zen kure* (Give me all the money, give me the money, give me the money)."   He is urging the sun to pay the debt.   When the rays of the sun make it too hot for him, he flies down again insisting, *"Kuree, kuree, kuree* (Give it, give it, give it)."

—Kanō Minzoku, No. 15, Part 4, p. 4
(Takamatsu-machi, Kahoku-gun,
Ishikawa)

In a different place they say that the meadow lark loaned money to a bunting.   The lark calls, *"Saa yare, saa yare* (Now hand it over, now hand it over)."   He is urging it to pay him back.   In that region they say the bunting answers, *"Chinchin kaeshimasho* (Let me pay back just a little)."

— Denshi Nomura, *Ōsumi Kimotsuki-gun Hōgen Shū,* p. 95
(Kimotsuki-gun, Kagoshima)

9. THE EARTHWORM WHO WEARS A REEL

Once upon a time an earthworm and a toad talked together about making dresses to wear.

The earthworm said, "I will choose fine thread carefully for mine because I want to wear a beautiful gown."

The toad said, "I will make mine of coarse thread because I want to finish mine and wear it quickly."

With that they set about their work as soon as they could. The toad made a coarse, rough dress in no time and put it on. On the other hand, the earthworm took time to weave her fine, beautiful thread slowly. As she worked, the thread got all crumpled and impossible to handle. At her wit's end, she finally began to wind the thread from the reel directly around her neck.

That is why even now a mark is left on her neck where she wound the thread. The toad is still wearing the same rough, soiled dress she wove long ago.

— Kiyomi Suzuki, *Naori-gun Mukashibanashi Shū,* p. 86
(Kamiida-mura, Ōno-gun, Ōita)

10.   THE OWL DYER

Long, long ago the owl was a dyer. He took orders from many birds and dyed all kinds of outfits for them as a business. In those days the crow was quite a dandy and flew around in a pure white suit.

The crow came to the owl dyer one day and said, "Dye my suit a color which cannot be seen anywhere else."

The owl took the order and dyed his suit charcoal black. He said, "In all the world there is not another color like this."

The crow was furious, but there was nothing he could do about it. He never forgot his grudge against the owl.

Whenever he sees the owl, the crow acts angry and bullies him, and that is why the owl hides deep in the forest even now, never coming out while the crow is awake. If the crow happens to find where he is hiding, he attacks the owl.

— Toshio Takagi, *Nippon Densetsu Shū*, p. 255
(Tairadate-mura, Iwate-gun, Iwate)

11.   THE WREN COUNTED AMONG THE HAWKS

Long, long ago a little wren came up to where all kinds of hawks had gathered together for a drinking bout.

"Take me into your band," he asked.

The company of hawks snubbed him and said, "If you want to be one of our crowd, catch us a wild boar. If you can do that, we will let you join our drinking bout."

The wren promptly flew away and hopped into the ear of a wild boar asleep in a thicket. The startled boar dashed off with the little wren beating around in his ear. Finally he struck his head on the corner of a rock and fell dead.

Then the little wren went back with a great swagger to the company of hawks and joined their drinking bout.

Now a huge hawk called a *kuma*-hawk (bear-hawk or bald eagle) felt that he could not be outdone. He rushed off to where two boars were running together. He grasped one boar with his left talons and the other with his right. The boars ran off in opposite directions and the greedy hawk's body was torn in half.

— *Minzoku*, Vol. I, No. 5, p. 191
(Hyōgo)

12. THE BADGER AND THE SNAIL

Long, long ago the badger went by for the mud-snail and the two of them went off on a pilgrimage to Ise.

When the last day of the trip came, the mud-snail turned to the badger and said, "How about it, old Badger? Just walking along this way is no fun. Why don't the two of us run a race from here to the Great Shrine of Ise?"

While the badger was getting ready to start, the alert mud-snail opened his shell and fastened himself onto the end of the badger's tail. That was how, without any effort at all, the mud-snail could run along as fast as the badger.

At last they reached the Great Gate of the Shrine, and the badger, feeling happy, whisked his tail. With a click half of the mud-snail's shell struck the stone wall and was broken off. He fell rolling onto the ground.

Show-off that he was, the sly mud-snail covered his pain and said, "Say, old fellow, you are late, aren't you? I got here first and have slipped off a shoulder to rest."

— Seiichi Moriguchi, *Kii Arita Dōwa Shū*, p. 11
(Arita-gun, Wakayama)

13. THE BADGER, THE MONKEY, AND THE OTTER

Long, long ago the badger, the monkey, and the otter set out together to visit the shrine of Yahiko. On their way they picked up things that had been dropped along the road. These were a piece of matting, a bag of salt, and about two quarts of beans. They talked over how to divide the things, but they couldn't agree at all upon a plan.

Then the shrewd badger suggested, "Master Monkey, how about taking this piece of matting and climbing up to the top of a tree over on the mountain? You could spread it out there and enjoy the view in all directions, couldn't you? Master Otter, how about you taking this salt to some pool where there might be fish and scattering it there? You could make the fish float up and then catch them, couldn't you? Then I would take the beans that are left and eat them."

The other two thoughtlessly agreed.

The monkey cheerfully carried off the piece of matting to the top of a tree and spread it out. He was about to enjoy the view, when he slipped and fell out of the tree, wrenching his legs. The otter found a pond and poured the bag of salt into it. Then he went into the water to look, but the salt burned his eyes, making them red and sore.

"We both certainly have a bad bargain on our hands. It's all because that badger wasn't fair," they complained as they set out for his house.

In the meantime the badger had eaten up every one of the beans. He and his badger-wife had fastened the husks of the beans into his fur and he pretended to be groaning.

"I ate all the beans and now I have broken out with boils," he whined. "It hurts, it hurts!"

The monkey and the otter were fooled again. They went away saying, "We are all in the same boat. There's nothing to do about it."

— Rekirō Sotoyama, *Echigo Sanjō Nangō Dan,* p. 41
(Minamikambara-gun, Niigata)

14. THE MONKEY, THE CAT, AND THE RAT

Long, long ago an old man and an old woman lived in a certain place. The old man used to wrap up the lengths of cotton cloth which the old woman had busily woven, and go peddling them about from town to town.

One day after selling the cloth, the old man was going along a mountain path alone. He saw a hunter who was about to shoot at a female monkey in a tree on the mountain in the distance. The monkey seemed to be clasping her hands in prayer, begging him not to fire. Thinking it a heartless thing for the hunter to do, the old man went up to try to stop him. The gun missed the mark and by accident wounded the old man in the shoulder. The hunter, seeing he had done a terrible thing, ran away.

Then many young monkeys appeared from somewhere and took care of the old man the best they could. They led him to the monkeys' home where they gave him a big feast.

At last the old man said, "My old woman will be worrying so I had better be going back."

The monkeys then brought out a treasure for him to show their gratitude. "This coin is called a monkey farthing," they said. "It is a very great treasure. We want to present it to our rescuer. If you place this upon your altar and worship it, you will become rich."

It was truly the way the monkeys said it would be. At home the old man was scolded hard by his old woman for returning without selling all of the cloth when it was so close to the end of the year. However, through the help of the monkey farthing they became rich in a short time.

Now there lived a bad man in the neighborhood. After he learned why the old couple had become rich so suddenly, he stole the treasure away when they didn't know. The old man and his wife were frantic and asked everywhere about it but couldn't find where it was.

Then they called Tama, the cat they kept at their house. "Now, Tama," they said, "you must look for the monkey farthing and bring it within three days. If you find it for us, there will be a big reward for you. If you fail to find it for us, it will be this," they concluded, drawing out a bright dagger.

As soon as he heard this, the cat dashed off and caught a rat and told him about it. "Now, Rat," he said, "My old master's treasure is missing. You must go and find it in three days. If you find it for me, I will spare you. If you fail to find it for me, I will eat you up, tail and all."

The rat thought it would be awful to be eaten, so for three days he went from house to house in the neighborhood looking for the monkey farthing. Finally he found it in a chest of drawers at the house of the bad man next door.

The rat gnawed a hole in the drawer and took out the coin, which he carried to Tama. In great delight, Tama picked up the coin in his mouth and brought it to the old man.

The old man, the old woman, the cat Tama, and the rat, all rejoiced together and prospered for ever after. *Medetashi, mede-tashi* (A formula for a happy ending).

—*Impaku Dōwa,* p. 68
(Yazu-gun, Tottori)

15. THE RICE-CAKE RACE OF THE MONKEY AND THE BULLFROG

Once upon a time a monkey and a bullfrog met in the mountains. With the approach of New Year, the cheerful sounds of mallets pounding rice-cakes could be heard here and there in the village.

"Say, old Bullfrog," proposed the monkey, "isn't there some way we could get a mortar of that rice-cake to eat?"

The two of them made up their plan there in the mountain, and then they made their way carefully down into the village. First the monkey went to the gate of the back yard of the village mayor's house and hid. A little later, the bullfrog came up and stole into the garden. Suddenly he flopped into the spring pond with a big splash.

The young people pounding rice in the yard heard the noise and shouted, "How terrible! Our Little Master must have fallen into the pond."

Everyone deserted the mortar and rice-cake to rush to the edge of the water. With the stage thus cleared, the monkey grabbed the mortar with the rice-cake in it and carried it easily up to the top of the mountain. The bullfrog made his way up slowly after him.

"Now, Bullfrog, old chap," suggested the monkey, "rather than for the two of us to divide the rice-cake, wouldn't it be better to roll it down from here, mortar and all? We could run after it, and the one who reaches it first could eat the whole piece. How about it?"

The bullfrog knew that he was slow-footed and that he would probably lose out, but he agreed.

With a shout of one, two, three, the mortar of rice-cake was sent rolling down to the bottom of the slope. The swift-footed monkey went flying right after it. The heavy-footed bullfrog went shuffling down one step at a time. As luck would have it, however, the rice-cake pitched out of the mortar un-noticed and was left dangling on a clump of bush clover on the way.

"This is a good stroke," said the bullfrog and promptly squatting beside the rice-cake, he began slowly chewing on it all alone.

Finding he had only chased an empty mortar, the monkey scrambled back up dejectedly. With his mouth watering, he hinted, "Bullfrog, old boy, how about us starting to eat it from this corner?"

"Why, this is my rice-cake," answered the frog. "I can eat it from wherever I like."

—Rekirō Sotoyama, *Echigo Sanjō Nangō Dan,* p. 114
(Minamikambara-gun, Niigata)

16. A LEAK-IN-AN-OLD-HOUSE

Long ago an old man and an old woman could not sleep on a rainy night. They lay awake talking together.

One said, "A leak in an old house is something to fear more than a tiger-wolf."

Now a tiger-wolf happened to be standing just outside the door and overheard this. "There must be some creature which is more dangerous than I," he thought. "I must be on the lookout."

Just then a horse thief was about to break into the house. Thinking the tiger-wolf was a horse, he climbed onto his back.

"This is awful. Now I am caught by that terrible leak-in-an-old-house," thought the wolf.

Quick as a flash he jumped up and ran away. He shook off the horse thief, who fell into a dry well by the side of the road.

A monkey came along there and asked the tiger-wolf, "What are you up to?"

"There is a monster called a leak-in-an-old-house hiding in this hole," answered the tiger-wolf.

"There isn't any such monster, is there?" said the monkey. "I'll find out for you."

The monkey, who is apt to be officious anyway, let his tail down into the dry well and felt around. The horse thief at the bottom of the well grabbed hold of the tail with a firm grip. When the startled monkey tried to pull his tail up, he pulled so hard that it snapped off at its base.

There is also this legend about when the monkey's tail began to be short.

— Toshio Takagi, *Nippon Densetsu Shū,* p. 254
(Aso-gun, Kumamoto)

17.   THE MONKEY BRIDEGROOM

Long, long ago an old man from a village was working alone in a patch of garden on the mountain-side.

The garden was so big and he had to work so hard that he declared, "Oh, even a monkey would do! If he would only come to help me, I would give him one of my three daughters as a bride."

Just then a monkey appeared and began to help the old man briskly in the garden.

"What an impossible promise I have made!" thought the old man.

After going home, the old man talked it over with his three daughters. The eldest daughter and the second became very angry, declaring they couldn't be made to marry a monkey.

Only the youngest daughter was a tender-hearted girl. She said, "If it was a promise, it cannot be broken, so I will go as the bride. All I want for my wedding is one big earthen jar. Please put lots of needles in it."

On the next day the monkey came in the morning all dressed up exactly like a bridegroom to take his promised bride. On his back he put the bride's belongings, the earthen jar and the needles, and they went off together, talking in a friendly way, toward the mountain where the monkey lived.

At the foot of the mountain there was a deep stream with only a slender log across it for a bridge. While they were crossing it, the monkey bridegroom spoke up and said, "If we have a boy child, what shall we name him? Since his father is a monkey lord, we could call him Sarusawa (Monkey Dell). If we have a little girl, let's call her Ofuji (Wisteria) because the wisteria in this valley are so lovely."

As they went talking along, the bridge was so narrow that with a bare touch of her hand the monkey fell into the stream and was carried away with the jar of needles still on his back.

Crying as he went, he sang a song like this, the words of which are still left:

Sarusawa ya, Sarusawa ya,
Ofuji no haha ga nakuzo kawai ya.
(Monkey Dell, Monkey Dell,
Wisteria's mother weeps. Oh, the pity.)

— Minzoku, Vol. I, No. 6, p. 180
(Hiba-gun, Okayama)

18. THE EAGLE'S EGGS

Long ago there lived in a village a farmer with an only daughter who was very beautiful. At the time to transplant rice he was looking over his bed of rice sprouts. He saw a snake chasing a little frog and crushing the young plants.

"Stop, Snake. Don't chase it," he called. "I will give you my only daughter if you'll stop."

The snake stopped chasing the frog and went away quietly.

From that night a handsome young bridegroom began coming to the daughter, arriving late each night and leaving early in the morning. Not knowing what kind of man he was, the father was uneasy. He called to an unknown soothsayer who was passing one day and had him tell a fortune.

The stranger said, "Your daughter has taken a bridegroom who is not a real human being and she is bearing him a child which is not really human. It may be that she will die very soon. There is only one way to save her. An eagle has built a nest in the top of the great tree on the mountain back of here and is laying three eggs in it. I advise you to ask your son-in-law to go and get the eggs and to try feeding them to your daughter."

That night when the young man came, the daughter said to him that she wanted to eat the eagle's eggs. He gladly agreed to climb up to get them for her, but while he was doing it, he unmistakably changed into the shape of a real snake. After he had brought two eggs down in his mouth and as he went up for the third, the mother eagle pecked the big snake to death.

When the old man came home to see, the fortune teller of the day before was there again. After he heard what had happened, the fortune teller said, "Then your daughter has been saved. The next thing to do is to give her wine sprinkled with peach blossoms on the coming festival of the third of March. She will gradually grow stronger. I am the little frog whose life you saved. I want to repay your kindness." Saying this, he went away with a hoppity-hop.

People began drinking peach-blossom wine at the festival of the third of March from that time.

— *Minzoku*, Vol. III, No. 3, p. 167
(Kishima-gun, Saga)

19. FROM A MEADOW LANE IN SPRING

Long, long ago a poor old man lived alone. By working hard day by day he barely managed to get along.

"Today is the eighth of April (Buddha's birthday), so I think I will take it easy at home for this one day," he said to himself.

However, something came up which made it necessary for him to go out after all. "Since I bought this bottle of wine especially for today, I will hang it at my side. I'll take it along and perhaps have a drink on the way," decided the old man as he set out alone.

The weather was bright and clear. Around him in the fields and on the mountains all kinds of flowers were bursting into bloom. When he started to cross a broad meadow, the old man felt that, since the weather was so fine and he was getting a bit tired, this would be a good place to stop for a cup of wine. Selecting a stone of the right size, he sat down on it. As he did this, he discovered a skeleton lying on the ground by his feet.

"Well, well, I don't know what sort of person's bones you are, but this is just right because I don't like to drink alone," the old man exclaimed. "I'll give you a cupful, too, and while we look at the view, let's enjoy the bottle together."

With these words the old man filled a cup to the brim and poured it over the skeleton. Then after enjoying himself for a while, drinking and singing songs, he stood up and started on.

The old man finished his errand and came back through the same field toward twilight that day on his way home.

He heard a voice from behind call, "Old man, wait a bit."

He looked back and saw a beautiful girl seventeen or eighteen years old.

"Today you have made me very happy," she said. "I have been waiting for you to come back so I could thank you. Three years ago on the twenty-eighth of this month, I suddenly became sick and died while I was crossing this field. My parents have been looking for me in all sorts of places, but because the spiritual bond between us is too faint, they haven't been able to find me. Until today I passed very lonely days. On the twenty-eighth, when

37

my memorial rites will be held, I want you to leave whatever work you have and come here," declared the girl. "I want you to go with me to my parents' home."

At last the twenty-eighth arrived, and because he had promised, the old man went to the meadow to see while it was still morning. There the beautiful girl was waiting, so they went together into the village near the meadow. The girl's home was a big mansion. A crowd of people from the village had gathered there on that day for the ceremony.

"I can never go into a place like this," protested the old man.

"If you hold onto my clothes as you go in," the girl assured him, "nobody can see either of us."

They slipped into the house easily and sat down in front of the family altar. Trays of dinner, complete with soup and wine, were brought into the parlor. Since the old man liked the wine, he drank it as fast as the girl poured it for him. He drank the wine and took all kinds of his favorite dishes.

The priests in the parlor and the invited relatives began to say to each other that it was strange how the food and wine were disappearing from their trays before they knew.

It finally came time to clear away the trays. A little maid servant dropped a plate. The master of the house scolded her hard. He said that it was an outrageous thing to do to a valuable dish.

When the ghost girl saw this, she turned to the old man and whispered, "I don't like such scenes. I am going back."

"Then I'll leave, too," answered the old man.

"It's all right for you, so please stay on," she replied and slipped away alone.

After the girl went out, everybody immediately began to see the old man's form. They all began asking him questions at one time.

"What sort of a person are you?"

"Where did you come from?"

"Why are you here in this parlor?"

Since he could no longer hide anything, the old man held back nothing and told everything that had happened.

The relatives were all very much astonished. The master and

his wife wept and said, "We pray you, lead us quickly to the meadow where our daughter is."

Thereupon the old man led the procession of all the company, even the priests, out to receive the bones. Then they performed the funeral rites once more.

The old man gave up his poor odd jobs, and with the kind assistance of the people at that house, he got along comfortably for the rest of his life.

— Kizen Sasaki, *Rōō Yatan*, p. 52
(Kamihei-gun, Iwate)

20. THE GOLDEN AX AND THE SILVER AX

Once upon a time there was an honest woodcutter who worked in the hills every day cutting wood. While he was working in a forest by a lake one day, he swung his ax so hard that it fell into the lake. He wondered what he could do, because without his valuable ax he could not work.

Just then a white-haired old man came up out of the water. He asked the woodcutter what he was thinking about so earnestly. The old woodcutter told how his ax had fallen into the lake.

"I'll go and get it for you," said the old man. He sank into the water and presently came out again carrying a beautiful golden ax. He asked, "Is this the ax you dropped?"

"That isn't the one," he answered.

The old man sank into the water again and this time he brought out a silver ax.

The woodcutter said, "The ax I dropped wasn't so beautiful. It was a plain iron one."

The old man went back into the water once more. This time he brought out the iron ax. "Is this it?" he asked and returned it to the woodcutter.

"That's it, that's it," cried the happy man and thanked him as he reached for it.

The old man said, "You really are an honest fellow. As a reward I am going to give you the golden ax and the silver one as well." With that he handed them to the woodcutter.

To get splendid gold and silver axes in addition to having his own back made the woodcutter overjoyed. He could not keep quiet about it and told his bad old neighbor.

That old man then set out to the forest thinking he would get the same for himself. He dropped his ax into the lake on purpose.

Just as had happened before, an old man came up out of the water and said that he would go and pick it up. With that he sank back into the water. Instantly he came out with a lovely golden ax. "Is this the one you dropped?" he asked.

The covetous old man looked as if he would leap for the ax and shouted, "Yes, that's it!"

Then the white-haired man got angry and said, "To a liar like you I will not give a golden ax or a silver ax or an iron ax."

With that, he just sank back into the water and did not come out again.

— Kiyomi Suzuki, *Naori-gun Mukashibanashi Shū,* p. 27
(Kujū-machi, now Kujūmiyako-machi, Naori-gun, Ōita)

21. THE LITTLE HAND-MILL THAT GROUND OUT GOLD

Long, long ago there lived two brothers near the pond called Mizoro-ga-numa in Ōshū. The elder brother was rather dull-witted, but the younger was quite shrewd. The younger brother made his elder brother go to the edge of the pond every day to cut grass.

Now it happened one day that a beautiful maiden came up out of the pond with a letter in her hand. "Please take this letter to the pond called Hachirō-ga-numa at the foot of Mt.

The Little Hand-mill...

Okomagatake," she said to the elder brother. "When you reach Hachirō-ga-numa, stand by the margin and clap your hands. A beautiful maiden will rise up out of the water. All you have to do is to give her this letter."

The young man promptly did as he was told. After he arrived at Hachirō-ga-numa with the letter, he stood on the margin and clapped his hands. Immediately a beautiful maiden appeared from the pond. She accepted the letter and read it.

"My elder sister at Mizoro-ga-numa is always receiving kindness from you, it says. Wait here for a little," she said, "while I go to get something mentioned in the letter."

She went back into the pond and soon returned with a little stone hand-mill. She said, "There are not two such treasures in all this world, but since my elder sister has said so, I will present it to you. If you put only one grain of rice into this and turn it, a grain of gold will come out. Only be sure, when you go home, dig a little pool—even a little one will do—in the corner of your yard. Every morning and evening dip some water from it and offer it to the little stone mill."

After saying this, she gave the hand-mill to the young man and went back into the pond.

The elder brother took the hand-mill and carried it to his own house. Every day he ground out a grain of gold and began to live an easy life.

Noticing that his elder brother did not go out to cut grass any more, the younger brother thought it strange that he was spending his days in ease. He spied on him and saw him turning that strange hand-mill.

While his brother was away, the younger brother found the tiny hand-mill in the corner of the family altar and brought it out. After putting a grain of rice into it and turning it, he was surprised to see a grain of gold come out. However, because he was greedy, he could not stop and leave it at that. Thinking that he would take a lot of gold at one time and keep it, he poured a whole bowl of rice onto the little hand-mill and tried grinding.

The little hand-mill tipped over and began rolling and rolling.

41

It rolled out of the house and into the little pool in the corner of the yard, completely disappearing from sight.

—Kizen Sasaki, *Esashi-gun Mukashibanashi*, p. 72
(Esashi-gun, Iwate)

22. LITTLE RUNNY-NOSE BOY

Long, long ago there lived an old man in Mayumi-no-sato far back in the mountains of Higo province. By going into the mountains to cut firewood and taking it to sell in the town of Seki, he barely managed to make a living every day.

One day it seemed that he could not sell the wood, no matter how hard he tried. He crossed and recrossed the bridge of the river which ran through the middle of the town as he went around trying to sell the wood, but there wasn't a single person who would buy it. Worn out at last, he stopped to rest at the middle of the bridge. He threw the bundles of wood one at a time into the deep channel of the stream. Then he said a prayer to the River Goddess and started to go home.

Strangely enough, just as he did this, a young maiden more beautiful than he had ever seen rose up out of the deep water and called the old man to stop. On her arm she carried a little child, a truly little child.

"You work hard every day and are honest," she said. "And today you brought and offered your firewood to the River Goddess. She is quite pleased and places this little child in your care as a reward. Take him and go. He is called Little Runny-nose Boy. He will give you anything you ask for, but in exchange you must be sure to offer him a dish of fresh shrimp served with vinegar three times a day."

After handing the child to the old man, the maiden sank again to the bottom of the river.

In great delight the old man carried Little Runny-Nose Boy to his home at Mayumi-no-sato. He placed the child on his altar shelf and tended him with great care.

Whether it was rice or money or anything else, whatever he could think of that he wanted, when he would barely ask for it, Little Runny-Nose Boy would make a noise like blowing his nose and bring it out before the old man's eyes.

"This house has become too dirty," the old man said. "Please bring me out a bigger new home."

Even such things as a house would come forth with a single noise from the child's nose, and it would be a finer house than he had been wishing for. A storehouse and all kinds of furnishings gradually came out, until in the space of a single month the old man was rich, quite different from what he had been.

No longer having to gather wood in the mountains, his only work was to go to town every day to buy shrimps for the dish. However, as the days and months went by, this single duty grew to be a bit of a bother.

At last he lifted Little Runny-Nose Boy down from the shelf and said, "Little Runny-Nose Boy, since I have nothing more to ask of you, please go back to the River Goddess. Give her my kind regards."

When he heard this, the little boy went out without a word. For some time he could be heard outside, snuffling his nose. In the meantime, the house, the storehouse, and all the things in them began disappearing one by one until all that was left was the shabby old house which had first stood there.

Frantically, the old man rushed out to drag Little Runny-Nose Boy back, but he could not see him anywhere.

— *Tabi to Densetsu*, Vol. II, No. 7, p. 20
(Tamana-gun, Kumamoto)

23. THE SNAKE SON

Once upon a time there was an old couple living in the town of Tōyama. They had no child and lived a lonely life by themselves.

One day when the old woman went to their storehouse to get rice, she found a little snake there. Frightened at this, the old woman called her husband and tried to get him to kill it. The old man said it wasn't right to kill a snake that was in the storehouse, but they would chase it out. They both chased it with brooms, but no matter what they did, it would not go out. It would just coil up in a corner. At last they decided to feed it rice and keep it as a pet.

At first having the snake made them feel uneasy, but gradually they became accustomed to it. They loved it and gave it the name Shidō. Just as they would call a dog or a cat, they would call it, "Shidō, Shidō!"

Shidō began to grow bigger and bigger until presently it ate as much as a quart of rice every day. After a few years it got so big that when it curled up in the storehouse, it filled it completely and there was not room to put anything in. Besides this, each day it would eat more than two quarts of rice. Since the old couple could not work hard enough to raise any more than that, they could no longer keep him. Finally they declared that if they kept Shidō any longer, they would starve to death. After they talked it over, there seemed to be nothing left to do but to part with him.

That night, however, the old man had a dream in which he was told that if he would care for the snake willingly, he would surely be able to live without any difficulty. He told his wife about what he had learned, so in spite of the hardship, they put up with the snake and went on caring for it. Shidō kept on getting bigger until at last he couldn't get into the storehouse. The old couple were reduced to hopeless poverty.

One day they faced Shidō and said, "We have cared for you this way all along for countless years and you have become very dear to us. It is unbearable to think that we are getting so old that we can not go on working and taking care of you.

You have grown so big that you can not even get into our store house any more. That is why we want you to go away and live somewhere else from today." They put their hearts into what they said, keeping everything of the past and future in mind.

The snake seemed to understand quite well and went gliding away out of sight.

Now it happened that in the town of Tōyama there was a river called Jintsugawa, which had such a strong current that from long ago an ordinary bridge could not span it. The river was crossed with what was called a boat-bridge, a row of boats with boards laid on them. One day a snake appeared coiled up at the approach to the bridge. When anyone came near, it would raise its head as though it were going to attack him. It was so frightening that nobody dared use the bridge and the whole town turned into an uproar. Then the feudal lord sent out a proclamation that he would give a big reward of money to anyone who would destroy the snake. He had tall signs posted here and there to that effect.

Every day the news of the snake spread further until one day the old couple heard about it. Thinking it might be Shidō, the old woman said she would go to the bridge and see.

He was even bigger than when he left home, but he certainly looked like Shidō so she decided to go up close to him. Although he had raised his head as though he was going to strike others, when the old woman came up to him, he lowered his head little by little. This was surely Shidō, thought the old woman. She began to admonish him, saying, "Look here, Shidō dear, don't you know you are worrying me by displaying yourself in a place like this? Go somewhere else and hide yourself."

Then she went home as fast as she could to tell her old man about it. The two of them returned together to the approach to the bridge.

"Look here, my Shidō," the old man said, "if you frighten folks at a place like this, can't you see they are going to hate us? Please, since we both ask it of you, hide yourself somewhere."

The snake lowered his head before them and listened. Presently he began to move and suddenly his whole length went leaping into the water of Jintsugawa. He swam upstream for about a quarter of a mile or so and then came swimming back. When he came where the old couple were standing, he bowed his head to them. Then the huge snake swam on down the stream into the open sea no longer to be seen.

According to the terms of his proclamation, the feudal lord gave an allowance to the old couple, enough for them to live in comfort for the rest of their lives.

Even if it is something like a snake that is looked after for many years, it feels gratitude and will want to repay it.

> — Riki Dobashi, *Zoku Kai Mukashibanashi Shū*, p. 102
> (Kuisshiki-mura, Nishiyatsushiro-gun, Yamanashi)

NOTE: The narrator of this tale said that he had heard it from a medicine peddler from Etchū (Tōyama Prefecture).

24. THE WATER SPIDER

Long ago in Ōshū a man went fishing in a pond at Handayama one summer day. He caught an unusually large number of fish and filled his fishing basket to the brim in a short time.

Since the day was very hot, the man soaked his bare feet in the pond. A water spider, which came out from somewhere, ran over the surface of the pond and fastened his thread onto the man's big toe. Very soon it came back and fastened another thread on the same place. Thinking this was strange, the man cautiously unfastened the thread from his toe and wound it around the willow stump beside him.

Presently a voice from the bottom of the pond shouted, "Jirō, Tarō, the rest of you, come here!"

To the man's amazement, all the fish in his basket leaped out together and got away. Then many voices joined in with a shout of *en-to-en-yara-saa* and right before the man's eyes the spider's thread began to be pulled. That thick stump was broken off at the root with a snap.

Since that time not a single man has ever cared to go fishing in that pond.

(Date-gun, Fukushima)

25. WHAT THE *YAMA-CHICHI* OBSERVED

Long ago there was a cooper in a certain place. While he was working outside one morning after it had snowed, a frightful monster with only one eye and one leg appeared from the mountain and stood in front of the cooper.

Seeing him, the cooper began to tremble and thought, "This must be the thing called a *yama-chichi*, which I have heard about in stories for a long time."

The apparition then said, "Say, Cooper, you're thinking I must be the thing called a *yama-chichi*, aren't you?"

The cooper thought, "How awful. He observes right away what I think."

Then the monster said, "Say, Cooper, you think it is awful because I observe right away what you think, don't you?"

After that whatever the cooper thought was observed until he was quite confounded. With nothing he could do about it, the man kept at his work, trembling violently all the time. Suddenly his numb hands slipped accidentally. The bamboo hoop sprang out in front of him and slapped the *yama-chichi* in the face.

The *yama-chichi* was taken by surprise. "These human beings are dangerous because they sometimes do things they are not thinking about," he declared. "There is no telling what will happen if I stay here."

He went stumping pellmell back to the mountain.

— *Kyōdo Kenkyū*, Vol. II, No. 6, p. 58
(Tottori)

26. THE WIFE WHO DIDN'T EAT

This is also a story about a cooper who lived in a village long ago.

One day toward evening when he went outside to relieve himself, the cooper said to himself, "Oh me, I wish I had a wife, one who didn't eat."

That very night a woman such as he had never seen before came and asked, "Is this where the cooper lives who wants a wife who doesn't eat? I am a woman who doesn't eat. Besides, I work very hard. Won't you please make me your wife?"

No matter how much the cooper refused, she would not go away. He had no choice but to let her stay as his wife.

To be sure, she worked well and she did not eat any meals, but for some reason or another the supply of rice had dropped fast before he noticed.

The cooper grew suspicious and decided to look things over. He prepared to go to work, but only pretending to leave the house, he climbed up into the loft to hide, and he spied on his wife instead.

Soon his wife put on a kettle, dipped out measure after measure of white rice from the sack into it, washed it, and began to build the fire to cook it. Then she went to the store-room and brought out lots of bean paste, heated a big pot of bean soup, and dipped it into a bucket. Next she took a board from the door and laid it across the entrance of the kitchen. From one end of it to the other she set a row of huge rice balls she made from the cooked rice.

After setting everything out, she took her hair down. There in the middle of the top of her head was a huge extra mouth. She tossed the rice balls into it one by one and then poured in the bean soup, a dipper full at a time. Right before the cooper's eyes, every bit of the rice and the soup was eaten up slick and clean. Then she tied her hair back up neatly and once more she looked like a nice kind of wife. This was a *yama-haha*.

"What an outlandish wife I have taken," thought the

cooper. "I must run her out quickly, by all means."

Toward evening the man covered his sandals with dust and came home as though he knew nothing. "No matter if you don't eat, you aren't the right kind of a wife for me," he said. "I'll give you anything, but please go away."

"Then I'll go, but please make me one big tub," his wife answered.

"A tub is easy enough," the cooper agreed, and he set about immediately to make one which he gave her.

The *yama-haha* caught the cooper off his guard and grabbing him, threw him into the tub. Then she lifted the tub onto her head and strode back up into the mountains. The cooper tried to get out of the tub to run away, but it was so deep that he couldn't jump out of it.

Gradually the path led into the mountains where big trees grew on one side, the branches brushing along the edge of the tub. The *yama-haha* stopped presently in the shade of a great tree to stand and rest a while. Thinking this was just the chance he needed, the cooper reached up and caught a hold of the overhanging branch and he pulled his body up out of the tub.

Not knowing this, the *yama-haha* started on into the mountains carrying the empty tub. The cooper had to take advantage of that to get away and started running back as fast as he could. The *yama-haha* seemed to notice this. She turned around and started right after him. He was afraid that she would catch up with him before he could get home, so he looked around for some place to hide.

Just there the iris grew thick on the sand bar of the mountain stream and with them there was a dense growth of mugwort. The cooper crawled in among the two kinds of plants, the *yama-haha* leaping in after him. Very fortunately the leaves of the iris stuck her right eye and the stems of the mugwort pierced her left eye, blinding her on the spot. She fell into the mountain stream and drowned. Her body was carried down the current.

That happened on the fifth of May and from that time it became an annual May Festival. On that day the two plants called iris and mugwort are always placed in the thatch of the roof, and the leaves are placed in water in which people bathe.

This is to prevent another such terrible experience like the cooper's.

— Hideo Oda, *Izawa-gun Mukashibanashi Shū*
(Izawa-gun, Iwate)

27. THE OX-DRIVER AND THE *YAMA-UBA*

Long, long ago an ox-driver put a big load of salted mackerel on the back of an ox and started for a mountain village to sell them. Unfortunately he met a *yama-uba* in the high pass on the way.

"Ox-driver, give me a mackerel," she called.

Reluctantly he pulled out a mackerel from the bundle and threw it to her, then hurried past. The ox was so slow that the *yama-uba* soon finished eating the mackerel and catching up with the driver, she teased for another. One by one, he had to throw them to her until all the big load of salted mackerel on the ox was eaten up.

When the mackerel were gone, she next demanded the ox and threatened to eat the man instead if he refused. Frightened out of his wits, the poor man left his ox behind and bolted. In less than no time the *yama-uba* crunched up the ox and gulped it down. Then she began chasing the driver.

"Now I'm going to eat you," she shouted.

This much, at any rate, the driver could not yield. He ran like mad until he came to the edge of a big lake. A huge tree was growing by the margin. He scrambled up the tree to hide, but unfortunately there were no leaves below him, and his form was reflected on the surface of the water.

The *yama-uba* came rushing up breathlessly. In her excitement she thought the reflection in the lake was the ox-driver and plunged in, looking everywhere for him.

Taking advantage of the time offered, the ox-driver came down out of the tree and started running again. At the foot of the mountain there was a house into which he dashed, only to find it was where the *yama-uba* lived. He climbed carefully up into the rafters and hid himself.

Soon after the *yama-uba* came out of the pond and came home. "I'm all worn out from teasing the ox-driver today," she said to herself.

Then she built a fire on the hearth and began toasting rice-cakes which she brought out. While the rice-cakes began to bake, the *yama-uba* fell into a doze. The ox-driver, who was hiding in the rafters, pulled out a stalk from the thatch, reached down, and picked up the rice-cakes one at a time and ate them.

The *yama-uba* woke up and roared, "Who took the cakes?"

With a tiny voice the ox-driver answered, "Fire God! Fire God!"

She picked up one piece of the rice-cakes which had fallen off the rack and was burned black. "If it was the Fire God, it can't be helped," she muttered.

Then she put a kettle on to heat some sweet wine. While she waited for it to heat, she fell asleep again. Taking another stalk from the thatch, the ox-driver sipped up all the wine.

The *yama-uba* woke up and roared, "Who drank this up?"

The ox-driver answered again in a tiny voice, "Fire God! Fire God!"

"On a night like this, it is better to sleep," declared the *yama-uba*. "Shall I sleep in the stone chest or the wooden chest? Stone is cold, so wood is better, I guess." Lifting the lid of the big wooden box, she climbed in and was soon fast asleep, snoring.

The ox-driver, who had been looking on, now came down cautiously from the rafters. He built up the fire on the hearth and put water on to boil. Next he brought out an awl and drilled holes in the lid of the wooden chest.

Inside the chest the *yama-uba* heard the sound and said to herself, "Tomorrow will be good weather because the drill bugs are singing."

In the meantime the ox-driver got the hot water and poured it through the holes and thoroughly revenged himself upon the *yama-uba*.

— Rekirō Sotoyama, *Echigo Sanjō Nangō Dan,* p. 119
(Minamikambara-gun, Niigata)

28. THE FLOWER THAT REFLECTED A HUMAN FORM

Once upon a time a childless couple lived alone in a certain place. The husband had no regular work and they lived a life of great poverty.

Feeling that it was hopeless to go on that way, the husband set out to look for work elsewhere one day. Along the way he met a stranger and thoughtlessly answered all the questions put to him about himself. The stranger, who was actually a bandit, went straight to the man's house. He went up to the wife, who was looking after the place, and said, "Your husband has asked me to take you away somewhere because he can no longer feed you." He fooled her and took her away to his own house.

When the husband came home, his wife was not there. He looked all around, here and there, but he could not find any trace of her. Day after day he went around looking for her until three years had passed. One day as he was hunting as usual for her, he came to the bank of a big river. There he met a white-haired old man who asked him why he had come.

The husband said, "I have been going around looking for my wife for three years."

The old man said, "Where she is it is impossible for you to find her."

"Old man, if you really know, please tell me," begged the man.

The old man explained, "Your wife was kidnapped by a great bandit and is living on a certain mountain at a certain place. When you go to that mountain, you will find a big mansion with an iron rod set beside the gate. Take it and strike the ground with it one, two, three times. You wife will come out."

The husband was relieved to learn this and went off immediately to that place. There really was a great mansion with an iron rod set beside the gate. He took it and hit the ground with it one, two, three times and out came his wife.

She was so happy that she thought she was dreaming. She took him into the house and set out a fine feast for him. "This wine is from year before last, this is wine from last year, and this is this year's wine." she said as she dipped out a cupful from each of the jars. Then she brought out the bandit's valuable sword and handed it to her husband. Although he might find it uncomfortable, she asked him to hide in an empty jar and she fastened the lid down over him.

When night came, the bandit returned. It happened that at this house there was a strange flower called *asunarō*, which reflected human forms. If a man came into the house, a male flower bloomed and if a woman came, a female flower bloomed. When the bandit came into his house, he noticed that two male flowers were open.

"There's another man in the house, isn't there?" he declared and started to hunt around.

The startled woman thought quickly and answered, "No, no, that is probably because I am pregnant and carrying a male child."

Delighted at that, the bandit exclaimed, "If it is as you say, we should have a celebration tonight."

His wife brought out strong wine and poured a lot of it for him. When she saw he was in a stupor, she put him into a hot bath. Leaving him there, she helped her husband out of the jar. He took the bandit's sword and killed him.

The couple carried the strange *asunarō* plant back to their region and presented it to the king. He was so greatly pleased with it that he promised them anything they wished as a reward. They asked him to lend them one thousand men and one thousand horses for one day. When he heard this, the king promptly granted them their request.

The couple led the thousand men and the thousand horses to the mansion of the bandit and packed up all his treasures. These they brought back and became great rich people.

— Ichirō Iwakura, *Kikaijima Mukashibanashi Shū*, p. 105
(Kikaijima, Ōshima-gun, Kagoshima)

29. "O SUN, THE CHAIN!"

Long, long ago a mother lived in a village with her three children. After she had left the three children to take care of the house while she visited the temple one day, a *yama-uba* appeared, disguised like their mother, pretending to have come back. A *yama-uba* can be known as soon as her hands are touched, but to fool the children she wrapped them in dried *taro* stems. Thinking that the hands were their mother's, the children opened the door and let her in.

The *yama-uba* took the littlest of the three children into her arms and went into a back room and lay down. Then she chewed him up and ate him. The two children lying in the next room heard that noise and asked what the *yama-uba* was eating. She took one little finger and threw it to them. When they saw this, the children knew at once that she was a *yama-uba*. They began to plan how to run away.

To begin with, the second child said that he had to go to the privy. The *yama-uba* told the older brother to open the door for him. In this way the two of them went out of the house. Then they cut notches with a hatchet in the peach tree by the well and climbed it.

The *yama-uba* came after them. While she was hunting all around, she looked into the well and discovered the children in the peach tree overhead. "How did you climb that tree?" demanded the *yama-uba*.

The older child lied and said, "We rubbed hair grease on the tree and then climbed it."

The *yama-uba* got the hair grease and rubbed it on the tree, but she couldn't climb it because she kept slipping.

The second child, watching her, laughed and exclaimed, "How can anyone climb a tree with hair grease rubbed on it! The way to climb is to cut notches in the tree with an ax and then climb!"

When she heard this, the *yama-uba* cut notches in the tree and started climbing.

Cornered at last, the two children lifted their eyes to the sky and cried out, "O Sun, send the chain!"

A rumble sounded and from Heaven a chain came down. Catching onto it, the two children climbed up to Heaven.

From behind them the *yama-uba* roared the same words, but this time a rotten straw rope came down from the sky. When the *yama-uba* caught onto it and started to climb, she fell from a high place into the buckwheat patch. Her head burst on a rock and she died.

The stalks of the buckwheat were stained by the blood of the *yama-uba*. That is why they have come to be such a bright red.

— Toshio Takagi,
Nippon Densetsu Shū, p. 267
(Amagusa-gun, Kumamoto)

30. THE MOUNTAIN PEARS

Once upon a time there was a mother who was bringing up her three daughters in a certain place.

One winter when it looked as though snow was about to set in, the mother became very ill. It seemed that each day or the next might be her last. At that point she called her three daughters to her bedside and breathing painfully, she said, "As a last wish, I would like to eat some mountain pears. Please, isn't there someone who would go and pick some for me?"

When the girls heard this, the oldest said, "Mother, I'll go and fetch them."

This made the mother very happy. She told her daughter what roads to take—this and then another—and that a beautiful bride would then appear before her. She told the daughter to follow the directions exactly as the bride would give them to her.

After promising to do as her mother said, the oldest girl set out. Presently a beautiful bride in lovely attire came out just as she had been told. She said to the girl, "Go ahead, *taan-tan.*" The girl continued in the direction she was taking. Then the bride said, "Come back, *taan-tan.*" The girl thought that since she had gone ahead exactly as she had been told to do, there was no reason to turn back. However, remaining true to her mother's instruction, she did as the bride said. Then the bride began repeating over and over, "Go ahead, *taan-tan,*" and "Come back, *taan-tan.*"

The girl obeyed, going and coming, until her patience wore out. At that rate she could never get to where the mountain pears grew. Besides, her mother was sick and waiting for the pears, and she could not go on doing this forever. She lost her temper and refused to obey the bride any more. She went straight ahead till she arrived at a crossroads. Suddenly the bride appeared before the girl and swallowed her head first in a single gulp.

At home the mother and her two daughters were waiting anxiously because the oldest one did not return. No matter how long they waited, she did not come. Finally the mother lost heart and said her girl must have been swallowed by the bride.

The second daughter said that she would go and see. Off she went. As this girl went along the same road, a lovely bride with beautifully combed hair appeared before her, too. In a sweet voice she sang, "Go ahead, *taan-tan*" and "Come back, *taan-tan*."

At first the girl followed her directions, going and coming, going and coming, but at last she, too, could no longer stand it. Paying no more attention to the instructions, she went on ahead too far, and she was swallowed up by the bride just as her older sister had been.

When at last the second daughter failed to return, the youngest said to her mother, "Now I will go this time and I will surely fetch the mountain pears. Please wait a little longer." Hurriedly she prepared herself for the trip and set out.

Just as before, the beautiful bride came out and sang, but the youngest girl did just as she was told. She crossed a meadow and returned, she crossed over a mountain and returned, doggedly going and coming. In the meantime she suddenly noticed the voice was only saying, "Go ahead, *taan-tan*."

As she went straight along there gradually appeared rice paddies. The water in the ditches by them ran along as though it was guiding the girl. She followed it and came to a meadow. Further along she found a single tree among the rushes and on it a lot of mountain pears. The happy girl ran up to it and began picking the fruit and cramming it into anything that could hold them. Then she ran back as fast as she could over the road she had taken.

She found her mother nearly dead and breathing with great difficulty. "Mother," she cried, "I picked the mountain pears and have brought them to you. Please eat some."

When she held them out, her mother, who had been lying in bed until then, got up and suddenly seemed well again. From that time the mother and child lived happily together.

— Takiko Sugawara, Collector
(Ichinoseki-shi, Iwate)

31. THE THREE CHARMS

Once upon a time the novice at a temple was sent to gather cryptomeria needles. While he was in the hills picking them up, a woman came out and asked, "Little Novice, what are you doing?"

He replied, "I am gathering cryptomeria needles." Then she helped him pick them up.

When it was getting toward evening, he started to return. The woman said, "I am your aunt. Next time, come home with me, for I want to fix good things for you to eat."

After the novice went back to the temple, he told the old bonze what had happened.

"Oh, no," said the bonze, "you don't have an aunt. That woman is a *yama-uba* and that is why you must not go to such a place."

The boy insisted, however, that he would go. Finally the bonze pulled out three powerful charms from inside the folds of his robe and handed them to the novice saying, "If you want to go that badly, I cannot stop you. If you should be in trouble, ask help of these charms."

The novice set out to visit his aunt's house in the hills. She let him in and told him to go to bed until she had fixed a feast for him. After a while he looked at her secretly. Over the hearth a big kettle was boiling and beside it his aunt had turned into a terrible *yama-uba* sharpening her butcher knife. The little chap remembered the words of the bonze and was sorry he had set out against his advice, but it did not help to think of that now. He wanted some way to escape and finally said, "Auntie, Auntie, please let me go to the privy!"

She got cross about it, but she let him go. Before he left, she tied a rope around his waist so she could hang onto him. Inside the privy the novice was trying to think of a plan when she called, "Boy, Boy, are you through yet?"

Just as he answered, "Not yet," a good idea flashed into his mind. He carefully untied the rope from his waist and tied it onto the post in the center of the privy. Then he stuck one of the charms he had received from the bonze onto it and said, "Please answer instead of me." This done, he started running away.

Unaware of this, the *yama-uba* called again, "Boy, Boy, are you through yet?"

The charm inside the privy called, "Not yet!" After a while it answered again in the same way.

Finally, the *yama-uba* lost her patience and yelled, "Are you going to stay there forever?" With that she pulled at the rope she had tied around his waist and the post holding up the roof of the privy came crashing down. When she discovered that the novice was not there, she roared, "You got away fine, didn't you?" In a great fury she started chasing him.

When the novice saw that the *yama-uba* was gradually gaining on him, he suddenly pulled out another charm and tossing it behind him, he called, "Big river, come forth!" As he did this, a big river appeared. While the *yama-uba* was crossing it, the novice kept on running.

After a while he saw that she was gaining on him again. He pulled out one more charm and tossing it behind him, he called, "Big mountain, come forth!" While the *yama-uba* was climing over the mountain, he barely managed to reach the temple.

Pounding on the door, he shouted, "Sir Bonze, Sir Bonze, please hurry and open the door!"

"Wait, wait," answered the old bonze as he put his hood onto his head and lifted himself up with a groan.

From outside the novice called, "Hurry, hurry!"

"Wait, wait," answered the old bonze as he fastened on his clogs and came down.

Stamping his foot frantically, the novice cried, "Hurry, hurry!"

"Wait, wait," answered the old bonze as he came tapping along leaning on his staff. At last he opened the door.

Dashing inside, the novice begged, "Quickly, hide me somewhere!"

The old bonze hid him inside the chest where the sutra scrolls were stored.

By then the *yama-uba* came rushing into the temple to hunt for the novice. At last she realized he was in the box of scrolls.

To vex her the bonze said, "If you put your hand into the chest, it will rot and if you touch it with your foot, it will rot."

Then he said, "How about comparing transformations with me? I will transform myself into bean-curd, so you try transforming yourself into bean-paste."

The *yama-uba* agreed and immediately turned herelf into bean-paste. In a flash, the bonze licked her up and ate her. She began thrashing around inside him and hurting him so much he could not stand it. He called for the novice to bring him some of the beans for the Setsubun Festival and ate them. They made him break wind and the *yama-uba* came jumping out then.

She ran back to the hills declaring there was nothing as frightening as the inside of a man's stomach.

— *Mukashibanashi Kenkyū,* Vol. I, No. 2, p. 44
(Miyakawa-mura, now Hachimandaira-mura,
Kazuno-gun, Akita)

32. THE OLD WINNOWING BASKET, THE OLD FURUSHIKI*, AND THE OLD DRUM

Once upon a time in a village there was a dilapidated old temple in which nobody lived. There was no bonze in charge and for some time it was rumored that ghosts came out in the temple at night.

Now it happened that one time a man came traveling alone and asked to be allowed to stay over night in the temple. The villagers told him that nobody had spent a safe night there and he had better give up the idea. This traveler was young and brave. Since there was no place else to stay, he wanted to be permitted to stay there anyway, regardless of what might appear. Saying so, he went in and rested.

Toward evening there was an unusually big noise which made the young man wonder if the ghosts were about to come out. He

---

* The narrator spoke in dialect, pronouncing this word in this unusual way.

sat still and stared ahead intently. Again, about midnight, there was another awful noise hard to describe. Along with the noise a drum came rolling out. While he was thinking a drum was a strange thing to appear, there was another terrible noise. This time a *furushiki* (a wrapping cloth) came out. Presently along with another big noise a winnowing basket came out. Just as he was thinking what unexpected things appeared — the biggest noise of all crashed. When he looked to see what had appeared this time, a chipped bowl came out of a cupboard.

He heard a voice say, "Well, now, since we are all here, let's start!" The drum, the *furushiki*, the winnowing basket, and the chipped bowl started to dance and sing,

Oh, the old winnowing basket, the *furushiki*, the old drum,
And the old chipped bowl from inside the cupboard,
Whatever and whichever, we don't care what,
Oh, *dokkoi, dokkoi!*

The traveler sat staring at them wondering how so many old things could gather together. Then the winnowing basket, the *furushiki*, and the old drum continued to repeat the song and the four danced on and on. Presently dawn began to appear. The old drum ran off to the inner room, the bowl went back to the cupboard, and the winnowing basket and *furushiki* both went off somewhere and hid.

In the morning the worried villagers came to see about the fate of the traveler. He was quite safe. He said that nothing much happened. Some old things came out and danced. With that he set out on his way again unconcernedly.

It is said that if old things are not thrown away, they come out this way.

— Hisako Maruyama, Collector
(Hatano-mura, Sado-gun, Niigata)

33. THE SUDDEN TONSURE

Long ago at a certain village a bad fox used to come out and do mischief.

"No fox can ever fool me," one man boasted.

When that man was coming home from somewhere, he saw a fox below the road on the sand bar of a river. It put broad magnolia leaves on its head and turned itself into a woman, and then pulling duckweed from the river, it rolled it up into the shape of a baby and held it in its arms.

"You dirty beast! You're trying to make a fool of me, aren't you?" the man said. "All right. Just see what happens."

He picked up a rock from the side of the road and threw it below at the child, hitting it squarely on the head and killing it with the single try.

The mother cried and raged, "Give me back the child the way it was!"

"Why, you're only a fox, aren't you?" he retorted.

That only made the woman angrier and she would not be pacified.

No matter how long the man waited, she didn't turn into a fox again, and the more he watched the more they seemed to be a real mother and child. He was finally convinced that he had done an outrageous thing. Although he apologized to her until he ran out of words, she couldn't be persuaded to forgive him in any such ordinary way.

"Then if nothing else will do, I'll become a priest to atone for this," declared the man.

The two of them went to a temple nearby where he explained things to the priest and had his head shaved.

The way in which the priest shaved his head hurt the man so much that he came back to his senses and looked around. The woman and her child were gone, and there was no temple, no priest. His hair, which the man thought had been shaved off, had really been chewed off by a fox.

— *Chichibu Tsukikawa Sonshi,* p. 31
(Chichibu-gun, Saitama)

34. THE NOVICE AND THE FOX

Long, long ago there was a novice called Zuiten at a mountain temple. Whenever the bonze went away and left Zuiten to take care of the temple alone, a fox would come to the entrance of the bonze's living quarters and call, "Zuiten, Zuiten!"

Once it was so provoking that Zuiten went around to the window of the Great Hall to look out. The fox was standing with his back to the entrance. When he would brush his fat tail on the door, it made a noise "zui" and when he would knock his head on the door, it made a sound "ten."

Being a clever novice, Zuiten quickly went back and stood by the side of the entrance. When he heard "Zui," he yanked the door back, so the fox, who was about to hit his head on the door for "ten," came tumbling onto the dirt floor of the quarters.

Shutting the door quickly, Zuiten went for a stick and started chasing the fox. While he was running after it, he lost sight of the fox. He went to the Great Hall to look, and the main image of Buddha seemed to have turned into two images. He could not tell which was the fox in disguise.

"Oh, well, you can't fool me that way," said Zuiten. "The main image at our temple always sticks his tongue out whenever we have services, so I can't make a mistake."

When he began beating the wooden gong and reciting the sutra, the fox-Buddha hurriedly stuck out a long tongue.

"Now then, I'll serve the food offering to our Buddha over at the quarters," announced Zuiten. "I'll leave the fox behind."

He hurried back to the kitchen and the mock-image came walking brazenly after him.

"First of all, I must give him a bath," said Zuiten, lifting the image into the cauldron over the hearth.

Then Zuiten tied the lid on securely and built up a good fire. By the time the bonze returned the fox was cooked whole and ready for him.

— *Uzen Toyosato Sonshi*, p. 251

(Toyosato-mura, now Sakegawa-mura, Mogami-gun, Yamagata)

35. THE ONE-EYED OLD MAN

Long, long ago there lived an old man and an old woman in Ōshū. The old woman had two eyes, all right, but the old man was one-eyed.

Late one day the right-eyed old man changed into a left-eyed old man and came home saying, "Now, Granny, I'm home!"

"This must be a fox," thought the old woman. Aloud she said, "You're home drunk again, aren't you? You always want to get into the straw rice-bag when you come home drunk, you know!"

"Oh, that again!" answered the old man and climbed into the straw bag by himself.

"After you're in the straw bag, you tell me to tie it up on the outside, don't you?" the old woman said.

"Oh, that again!" replied the old man and meekly let her tie him up.

"When I get a rope on this way, you always say to put you on the fire shelf and smoke you, don't you?" said the old woman.

"Oh, that again!" answered the fox again.

Then the old woman swung the fox onto the shelf over the hearth and built a big fire, plaguing him. She deliberately broiled fish and ate her supper alone so he could smell the good things. While she was doing this, the real right-eyed old man came home, and the left-eyed one on the shelf was cooked into fox soup.

— Kizen Sasaki, Rōō Yatan, p. 188
Kamihei-gun, Iwate)
(Tsuchibuchi-mura, now Tōno City,

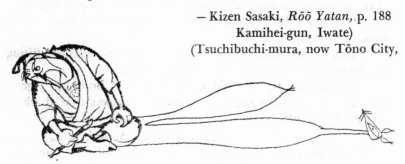

36. TANOKYŪ

Once upon a time there was an itinerant actor named Tanokyū. He left his mother alone at home and was going around looking for work.

A message came to him that his mother was ill. Being a filial son, Tanokyū decided to go back to his town as fast as he could. By the time he started up a long hill leading to the foot of the mountain, the sun was about to set. At the teahouse at the foot of the mountain the old woman said, "When the sun sets, a big python comes out in the mountain. You could never cross the mountain if you start up now so you had better stay here all night."

In spite of the old woman's warning, he did not heed it. Instead of spending the night there, Tanokyū went climbing up the road without heeding her because he wanted to get home quickly. While he stopped at the pass to rest in a little shrine, a big white-haired old man came out.

"Who are you?" asked the old man.

He replied, "Tanokyū."

The old man misunderstood and thought he said *tanuki,* a badger, and he declared, "If you are a badger, you should be clever at transformations. Won't you show me one? To tell the truth, I'm not a human being. I'm a python."

Tanokyū wondered if this was that python and he became so frightened inwardly that he hardly knew what to do. However, since he had several masks with him that he used in performances, he took out a woman's mask, put it on, and did a little act.

The python looked on with admiration and declared, "You are better than I thought you would be." After that he began to talk about all kinds of things. Finally he asked, "What do you hate the most?"

Tanokyū replied, "I hate those things called little gold coins the most. What do you hate?"

The python said, "I hate nicotine and the puckery juice of persimmons. If that gets onto my body, I turn numb and cannot move. Since you are a badger, I'll tell you, but promise not to tell any human being." Then he suddenly disappeared.

Tanokyū was frightened, but he thought he was lucky to have heard what he did. He ran down the mountain without stopping. It was already daylight when he reached the foot and he met a woodcutter starting out to work. He told the man what had happened the night before. The woodcutter said that they should take the word to the villagers immediately and destroy the python. Everyone gathered nicotine and puckery persimmon juice together and set out. The python, however, knew about that and escaped from the mountain.

He thought this had all happened because that badger talked too much. He resolved to take revenge. He set out and found Tanokyū's house. "Just figure this is to get even with you for the other day," he shouted as he threw a great pile of gold coins through the gable of the roof and went off.

— Kazuo Katsurai, *Tosa Mukashibanashi Shū*, p. 95
(Higashitsuno-mura, Takaoka-gun, Kōchi)

37. COMPARING DISGUISES

Stories about foxes and badgers who can transform themselves in various ways and fool men are heard in many villages. Among those foxes and badgers who are clever at disguises there are some with names like people.

It seems that once upon a time a fox named Ohana and a badger called Gombe lived in a certain village. One day Gombe Badger met Ohana Fox and said, "Miss Ohana, I hear you are very clever at disguises. Why don't you and I have a contest and compare disguises?"

Ohana Fox had always been proud of her way of doing disguises and she was secretly delighted at this. She promptly agreed to it.

If they were going to have a try, the sooner the better they thought. Agreeing to meet the next night on the grounds of Myōjin Shrine, they parted from each other. Each wanted to astonish the other and worked out a good plan, waiting for the coming night.

Ohana thought, "No matter how clever Gombe Badger is at transformations, he cannot keep up with me." She set out disguised as a beautiful bride. As she started to pass under the *torii* to enter the Myōjin grounds, she saw a freshly steamed dumpling that somebody had dropped there. The steam was rising from it and it looked temptingly delicious. Forgetting that she should be acting like a bride, she put out her hand, picked it up, and started to put it into her mouth.

"Miss Ohana, Miss Ohana," it said, "I won." Gombe had transformed himself into a dumpling and fooled the ever greedy Ohana Fox.

It is said that even a fox is fooled this way and defeated by a badger.

— Toshio Iwasaki, *Iwaki Mukashibanashi Shū*, p. 62
(Taira-shi, Fukushima)

38. THE CAT AND THE HUNTER

There was once a cat that enjoyed special attention at a certain hunter's home. It had lived so long that it had reached the age of twenty and it had grown as big as a dog. It got into all kinds of mischief which nothing could stop. It would open a cupboard door and take out fish, it would chase dogs, and finally it even took to jumping onto children. Its pranks became so rough that the hunter's wife could stand it no longer and she got angry. One day when she caught it stealing fish, she struck it sharply as she scolded it. The cat went off howling with pain and looked as though it would get even some time.

One day when the husband was going to go hunting as usual in the mountains, he set the casting pot on the fire of the open hearth, melted lead, and poured it into the mold to make his bullets. At that time the cat sat on the rim of the hearth intently waching what his master was doing. When a bullet was finished, the cat would lower its head and nod. When another was made, he would lower his head and nod again as though he were counting the bullets. The hunter made thirteen bullets.

Now the hunter did not notice what was going on. He took the bullets he had made and his gun and set out for the mountains. As he went farther and farther into the hills, he saw a strange kind of animal he had never seen before sitting on a rock. "Bang," the hunter promptly fired a shot. He was sure the aim was good and that the bullet hit the mark, but the animal just casually stood up and then sat down as though it was not aware of anything. Thinking this was strange, the hunter took another shot. This time he was quite sure it hit the mark, but again the animal simply stood up and then sat down. The vexed hunter began firing one after another, "Bang, bang," but the animal sat unconcernedly. At last he had shot all thirteen bullets he had made that morning.

Now this was a problem. He thought at this rate the animal must be some evil spirit in disguise planning to devour him when his bullets were spent and he wondered what he should do. It happens that hunters always carry a charm bullet made of iron next to their skin. There was nothing left to do but to shoot this so he took out the bullet and after taking careful aim, he fired. Strangely enough, this time with a single shot the animal toppled over and died.

When the hunter hurried up to the top of the rock to see, wasn't it that old cat they kept at his house that the bullet had hit and killed! And the thing rolled over beside it was none other than the lid of the tea kettle from his house which they used every day. The hunter stood there and nodded his head to himself exclaiming, "I see!"

The cat had stolen the lid of the tea kettle and held it up with its two paws to catch the bullets, hiding himself behind it and then casually sticking his face out from behind it. Feeling safe because it had counted thirteen bullets made that morning, it had not protected itself from the fourteenth bullet, and that last bullet had killed it. If the hunter had not had the charm bullet, there is no telling what would have become of him.

— Riki Dobashi, *Kai Mukashibanashi Shū,* p. 299
(Kuisshiki-mura, Nishiyatsushiro-gun, Yamanashi)

39. THE PILE IN THE HARBOR

Long ago in the harbor of Heisaka in Mikawa there was a bad badger who was always worrying boatmen. The worst trick the badger played was to disguise himself as a pile at which boatmen would moor their boats. When they went ashore to have a good time, he would take their boat off somewhere. There really were no piles in the harbor at Heisaka, but boatmen who came from other places in the evening would not know of the badger's trick. They would think that they had found a pile in just the right place and unwittingly tie up their boats, which later would go floating off.

Learning their lesson from the tricky badger, gradually fewer and fewer came to Heisaka for their fun. Some brave spirits at that place, however, decided that they would stamp out the badger once and for all.

One night when there was a full moon, a party of three or four young men hid ropes and sticks in a boat and rowed out. Only in the shadow along the embankment it was dark. Otherwise, it was a night in which the whole surface of the water spread out shining and white.

"This is a good place to land, but there aren't any piles here," one of the young men said in a loud voice on purpose.

Suddenly a fat pile appeared near the embankment.

The young men exchanged glances but pretended not to notice it at all. They rowed near it and then made believe they would pass.

A tiny voice from the water piped up, "Pile, Pile." The badger is naturally a bit stupid. He was impatient because nobody

69

seemed to notice and that was why he called in such a way.

"Oh. There is a thick pile, isn't there?" the young men said laughing. "We did not notice it before."

So saying, they got the rope out of the boat and quickly tied up the pile. The rope was twice as long as the one they usually used and they wound it round and round the pile, tying it securely to the boat. Next they took out the sticks and gathered around the pile, hitting it.

Suddenly the pile began to cry and the fact that he was in disguise came out. At last the bad badger was dispatched. *Medetashi. Medetashi.*

(Hazu-gun, Aichi)

40. MISOKAI BRIDGE

Once upon a time a pious, honest old charcoal maker named Chōkichi lived in a village called Sawakami at the foot of the west side of Norikuradake. One night he saw the following dream. A white-haired old man appeared by Chōkichi's pillow and told him that if he went to Misokai Bridge at Takayama, there would be something good.

Chōkichi promptly loaded charcoal on his back and selling it as he went along, he finally arrived at Takayama. For a whole day he stood by the bridge to see, but nothing good or out of the ordinary happened. Nevertheless, thinking something might happen yet, he went back day after day until the fifth day.

There was a single house standing there by the bridge where *tōfu* was made. The owner came out and asked why Chōkichi stood staring blankly at the bridge every day. When Chōkichi told about his dream, the *tōfu* maker laughed. He declared, "Even if you had such a worthless dream, there must be something the matter with you to be standing here day after day in such a place as this. I myself had a dream very much like that the other day. It was a dream about a man named Chōkichi who lives at Sawakami at the foot of Norikuradake and a treasure buried at the roots of a certain cryptomeria tree by his house. I do not even know that there is a village with such a name and if I did, how can anyone trust a dream. You had better hurry back home and stick to making charcoal."

When Chōkichi heard this, he concluded that this was the good thing mentioned in his dream. Alternating between feeling of surprise and joy, he thanked the *tōfu* maker heartily and hurried back to his village. As soon as he reached home he began to dig at the roots of the cryptomeria tree beside his house. Out came a great heap of gold and silver coins and treasures. In an instant he became a *chōja*.

The villagers called him Fukutoku Chōja, which means the *chōja* with great blessings and virtue.

— Shirōsaku Sawada, "Zoku Hida Saihō Nikki,"
Minkan Denshō, Vol. IV, No. 7, p. 2
(Takayama-machi, now a city, Ōno-gun, Fukui)

Note: Concerning the story connected with Misokai Bridge at Takayama in Hida, there are various similar examples in Japan and abroad. They all come into classification as tales about bridges. A brief explanation of this is in *Mukashibanashi Oboegaki*, but a word will be added here about the name Misokai Bridge.

According to the research of the collector of the tale, Shirōsaku Sawada, the author of "Zoku Hida Saihō Nikki: Misokai Bashi Gobun" in the reference above, until about 200 years ago there was still no bridge there, but a raft was fastened together and used for crossing. Later a generous family cut a large cryptomeria tree and made a log bridge. It happened that there was a *miso* maker called Rokubei there whose product tasted good and was cheap. Many people came across the log bridge to buy *miso* beyond the river. In no time it came to be called Misokai (Buying Miso) Bridge. But this log bridge was low and would drift down when the water would rise a little. Later, the approach to the bridge was built higher and the bridge was made of boards. During the Meiji Era and until the first years of the Taisho Era, the name of Misokai

Bridge was used, but in Taisho, when it was repaired it was called Ikada (Raft) Bridge and this name was carved on the post of the handrail. However, most people of that time continued to call it Misokai Bridge. At present, unless a person is fifty or sixty years old, he does not know that Ikada Bridge was ever called Misokai Bridge.

41. THE BOY WHO HAD A DREAM

A young lazy boy once had a dream. It was such a good dream that no matter who asked he would not tell it to anyone. The men around thought that if they took him to the chief of the village he would tell it, so they took him there but he would not tell. If he were in the presence of Daikoku Sama he would tell, they thought, but even there he would not. Daikoku became angry and had his servants drive him away.

The lazy boy, thus driven off, ran until he came to a lonely house into which he dashed only to find an old she-demon there. In reply to her angry demand to know what business brought him there, the boy told her truthfully why he had been chased away. The she-demon urged him to tell her what the dream was. When he refused, she offered to give him a fan by which he could fly up into the sky if he would tell her. He said he would have to try it first and if he could fly well, he would tell the dream, so she handed the fan to him. He took it and as he began slowly to fan, sure enough, he began to float up into the air. He kept on until he was high in the sky and so he escaped from her.

Presently he came out over water. As he flew over the open sea, he began to get tired. Looking down to find a place to rest a bit, he saw a small island and descended to it. While he was resting he noticed the island was beginning to sway. When the frightened boy looked closely, he realized the reason was because what had looked like an island was actually the back of a great whale. After the whale heard from the boy all that had happened, he said he would give the boy strange needles if he would reveal his dream. If he would prick anything, no matter how threatening, with one, he could kill it, and with the other he could restore life to something that was dead. The boy said he would not tell his dream until after he tried them. He pricked the whale with the needle that would kill something. The whale died. Then the boy used his fan and flew toward the mainland.

Where he happened to light was a castle town. All through the town there seemed to be an air of gloom and people looked sad. Asking the reason, the boy learned the daughter of the feudal lord had died the day before and everybody was in the midst of mourning. He told various people in the town that he knew a certain art by which he could restore a dead person to life. This report spread through the town and the feudal lord hastily sent a messenger to the boy to ask him to restore his daughter to life.

As soon as the boy arrived at the feudal lord's estate, he was led to the room where the lady lay. He set a golden screen around the bed of the young woman, who seemed still to be sleeping. He went behind the screen and began to chant, "Golden *hagu, hagu,* golden *hagu, hagu.*" He took the needle he had received from the whale and pierced her body. When he did this, the tint of blood began to creep into the face of the girl who was supposed to be dead. Her eyes opened wide and she came back to life.

Needless to say, the feudal lord and all the rest were overjoyed. Immediately the whole town was in an uproar, celebrating with a frenzy of joy. Saying that the young man was the guardian of the girl's life, the feudal lord urged him to be her husband, but he refused.

In place of that, he received a great amount of money as a reward and returned home where he lived peacefully with his parents.

— Tetsushiro Mutō, *Akita Gunyū Gyotan,* p. 119
(Miyasawa, Arakawa-mura, Senhoku-gun, Akita)

42. NETARŌ SANSUKE

Once upon a time there was a man called Netarō Sansuke, who did nothing but sleep from morning to night.

One morning, for some reason or another, he got up while it was still dark and went into the hills. In the evening he returned with a pheasant he had caught. He shut himself up alone in his room doing something until the evening of the next day, when he came out and went off somewhere.

The head of that village was called Genzaemon. He had a beautiful daughter called Omiyo San. Sansuke climbed up into the fir tree in the yard of the village head and waited for Genzaemon.

About the time it was getting dark Genzaemon returned. Just as he passed below the fir tree, Sansuke called from above, "Here, Genzaemon, if you do not take Netarō Sansuke as your daughter's husband, within three days I'll burn your house down." While he said this, he tied a lighted lantern onto the tail of the pheasant he had brought along and heading it westward, he let it fly off.

Genzaemon thought this was surely a revelation from the god of Izumo. On the next day he set out for Netarō Sansuke's house to ask him to marry Omiyo.

Thereupon Sansuke became the son-in-law of the head of the village, and he spent the rest of his life in ease, lying in bed.

— Isamu Isogai,
Akinokuni Mukashibanashi Shū, p. 58
(Takada-gun, Hiroshima)

43. DAMBURI CHŌJA (DRAGONFLY CHŌJA)

Long, long ago in the farthest region inland in Ōshū, there was a fabulously rich man called Damburi-chōja. His household numbered three thousand and at his house nearly five hundred bushels of rice were cooked each day. Because the water which washed the rice was drained into the Yoneshiro river, even now that river's water is a clouded white.

Damburi-chōja went to the capital city to apply for a *chōja's* seal.

"To be a *chōja,* you must possess a treasure which has been bestowed by heaven. The greatest treasure that a man has is a child-treasure. Do you possess such a child-treasure?" he was asked.

"Through my faith in Dainichi Nyorai of Azukizawa, I was blessed with an only daughter," he replied. "I have brought her with me on this occasion to see the sights."

When she was called out and presented, the maid was indeed as beautiful as a rare jewel. It is said that later she became a high ranking consort.

In his youth, Damburi-chōja was just an honest, hard working farmer. He went into the mountains and set up a little hut in which he and his wife lived. Together they farmed little patches of garden which they dug on the mountain-side.

It happened one day that while they were resting at noon, his wife was watching him lying asleep with his mouth wide open by the side of the garden. She saw a dragonfly come flying from the foot of the mountain opposite, a second and third time, circling above the man's head and around his mouth. She thought it very strange.

Then Damburi woke up and said, "I was dreaming just now that I was drinking such good wine. I can't think how to tell you how good it was."

His wife then told him about the dragonfly.

They wondered what the meaning could be. The two of them went around the mountain to look. There they found a clear spring flowing from below a rock. Dipping some up, they discovered that it was a spring of wine. Furthermore, the same mountain yielded an endless amount of gold. They dug and dug it and carried it home. Soon they became great, rich people.

"Damburi" is a word in Ōshū which means dragonfly. People called him Damburi-chōja, the Dragonfly-chōja, because one had showed him how to become a chōja.

— *Kazuno Shi,* p. 51
(Kazuno-gun, Akita)

44. WARASHIBE CHŌJA

Long ago a poor man and a rich man were neighbors in a certain place. The rich man had an only daughter and the poor man an only son.

One day the poor man's son went to the rich man's house and asked, "Is there any reason why you will not give your daughter to me as a bride?"

The rich man replied, "I won't give my daughter to a poor man like you, but if you can earn enough to be a millionaire, starting with this one piece of straw, I might do it." With that he handed him the piece of straw.

The young man accepted it and left the rich man's house.

Outside there was a strong wind blowing and threatened to become a storm. As he passed a certain house he saw the old man there having a hard time trying to hold up a plant with his hands that was about to topple over in the wind. The young man used the straw he was holding to fasten the plant firmly for him so it would not move. The delighted old man gave him a banana leaf as thanks.

The young man accepted it and went on his way. Presently it began to rain. At that time he met a man who had gone to buy some *miso* and was on his way home. There was no lid on the vessel he was carrying it in and the rain was landing on the *miso.*

The young man said, "It won't do for your *miso* to get wet, will it?" He gave him the banana leaf he was carrying.

The man gladly covered his *miso* with the leaf and in thanks he gave the young man one lump of it.

In the meantime it was getting dark so the young man asked a blind old woman who was living alone to let him put up there. It was a destitute place. She had some rice but nothing to go with it. He took out the *miso* he had received and gave it to her.

The old woman took one taste of it and jumped up with a shriek. "Oh, how salty," she cried.

It was so salty that at the moment she leaped up, her eyes opened and she had the good fortune to be able to see once more. Overjoyed at this unexpected event, she wanted to give the young man something as thanks, but she didn't have anything suitable. All she had was an old razor that had formerly belonged to her old man. She gave it to him with heartfelt thanks.

The young man accepted it gratefully and bade the old woman farewell. As he went along he met a *ronin,* a wandering samurai. The man said he was a samurai, but the hair on the shaven portions of his head and his beard had grown thick by then and he looked exactly like a beggar. The young man felt sorry for him and with the razor he was carrying he shaved the man's head and beard neatly. The samurai looked so splendid he seemed like another person. He was delighted and gave the young man a sword.

The young man fastened the sword to his side and went on his way. This time he met a feudal procession. When he knelt on the ground and bowed, one of the samurai in the midst of the procession stepped out directly toward the young man. Wondering what had happened, he raised his face.

The samurai said, "That sword you have at your side looks like a splendid piece of craftsmanship. You may have whatever you ask for it if you will hand it over. My lord wishes it."

Then and there the young man became a far wealthier man than he had ever expected. He went back home and called upon the *chōja* next door. The *chōja* gave his daughter to him as he had agreed and the two lived lovingly together ever after.

— Asatarō Yamaguchi, *Ikinoshima Mukashibanashi Shū* (new), p. 170

(Shihara-machi, now Gonoura-machi, Iki-gun, Nagasaki)

45. KOGORŌ, THE CHARCOAL MAKER

Long ago the famous *chōja* at Mano in Bingo province was formerly a humble, hard-working youth called Kogorō, the charcoal maker. He built a little hut at Uchiyama in Mie and lived alone, baking charcoal for a living.

A beautiful maiden from the capital came to call at the lonely little hut of Kogorō, the charcoal maker, one day.

"I have received an oracle from Kannon Sama at the Kiyomizu temple, and that is why I have come to your house to be your bride," she said. "Please let me stay at this little house now from today."

"I am very happy that you have come all the way from the capital especially to be my bride," answered the young man, "but there is not even enough rice for the two of us to eat tonight in this little house."

"Then please go to town and buy some rice," the maiden said. She drew out two gold coins from a brocaded bag and gave them to Kogorō.

Holding the gold coins in his hand, he went down the mountain to town to look for food. A brook ran at the foot of Uchiyama. On its banks a forest of purple willows grew thick, and in their shadows lay a quiet pool. A pair of mandarin ducks was playing on the surface of the water as Kogorō walked along the path through the forest. When his eyes lighted on them, he stopped still. Using the coins which he had in his hand as pellets, he threw them at the birds. He aimed well, but the ducks flew away, and the coins sank to the bottom of the pool.

Kogorō went back up to his little hut in the mountain because there was nothing else for him to do. "I found some water birds on the way," he said to his bride. "I thought I would catch them for you, but I missed them."

When she heard this, the young bride was dismayed.

"Those were valuable treasures called *koban*," she explained. "With only that many you could have bought lots of rice and fish and fowl. What a pity you did it!"

This was the first time that Kogorō, the charcoal maker, had ever heard of such things. He was very much surprised. "I had no idea that those stones were such priceless treasures," he declared. "In the hills behind this hut there is any amount of little stones of that color scattered about."

Hurriedly the two of them lighted pine torches and went to see. It was exactly as Kogorō had said. All the little stones in the whole valley were pure virgin gold. They gathered them and carried them to the little hut. They put them inside, but in a short time the house was so full of them that they piled them up on the outside.

When the people in the town and village heard of it, they all came one after another, bringing all kinds of things to sell. In order to get a share of the gold, they all came to work for Kogorō and his wife.

Then Kogorō established the big estate at Uchiyama in Mie. He also built a temple for Kannon and worshipped her. Just as with Damburi-chōja, the *chōja* of Ōshū, a little girl as beautiful as a rare jewel was born, and later she was sent to the capital as a consort. The household continued to prosper, but because Kogorō had been a charcoal maker formerly, people called him the Charcoal-maker *chōja*.

Riyō Shū, p. 641
(Utsuki-shi, Oita)

46. THE GOLDEN CAMELLIA

Long, long ago there lived a quick-tempered feudal lord. One time when he was giving a banquet which lasted late into the night, he noticed his wife unconsciously yawning. He became furious at this. He had her set adrift, exiled in a tiny boat built for only one. It was tossed about in the waves and at last touched the shore of a little island.

Rescued by the islanders, the lady learned to live a totally different kind of life from what she had known, but in a short time she gave birth to the feudal lord's child. He was a child as lovely as a jewel, but he was brought up exactly like the children on the island.

When the boy was twelve years old, it seemed strange to him that although other children all had a father and a mother, he alone had no father, but only a mother. He asked his mother why this was.

"Then I'll tell you," said his mother. "You really are the child of a feudal lord in a distant country. While I was carrying you I committed the sin of yawning and was exiled at sea."

This was the first time he had heard this. He faced his mother and said, "I am going to go to meet my father immediately." He set out on the journey.

Presently he came near his father's castle. In the mountains around there many camellias were blooming. For some reason he broke off a sprig of camellia. Holding it in his hand he went by the entrance to the castle shouting, "How about a golden camellia? Do you want a golden camellia?"

The feudal lord noticed the voice and ordered, "Bring that fellow here!"

In less time than it takes to say, the servant brought him in with a sprig of ordinary camellia in his hand.

The feudal lord rebuked him saying, "Anyone walking around waving such a thing and calling it a golden camellia is an insolent fellow!"

The boy replied, "No, no, this looks like an ordinary camellia, but if somebody who never yawns would plant it, golden camellias would bloom on it."

The feudal lord exclaimed, "Now what a silly thing to say. There is not likely to be anyone in the world who does not yawn."

Without hesitation the boy said, "But your lordship exiled your precious lady for yawning a single time, didn't he?"

The feudal lord was startled and suddenly realized the wrong of accusing his wife in a flash of temper. He sent for her to return from the island and the three of them spent happy days together.

— *Fukui-ken Kyōdo Shi*
(Fukui)

47. UGUISUHIME (NIGHTINGALE PRINCESS)

Long, long ago there was an old man in Suruga province. He made his way in life by going into the mountains to cut bamboo and making it into all kinds of trays and things which he sold. In old books he is called *Taketori-no-Okina* and *Mizukuri-no-Okina*.

This Mizukuri-no-Okina went into a bamboo grove one day, and there he found an especially radiant egg in a nightingale's nest. When he carried it home carefully and set it down, it broke open by itself. From inside there was born a very tiny, lovely princess. Because she was born from a nightingale's egg, the old man named her Uguisu-hime or Princess Nightingale. He brought her up as his own child.

As Uguisu-hime grew up, she became a most beautiful maiden and her beauty shone so radiantly that she was also called Kaguya-hime or Princess Radiant. The sections of bamboo which Mizukuri-no-Okina cut and brought home were always full of gold. In a short time the old man who had been so poor became very rich.

All kinds of men came seeking to marry the beautiful daughter of the rich man, but they would have to go away disappointed because they could not answer difficult questions which had been put to them by the father and his child. The ruler at that time heard about the lustrous beauty of Kaguya-hime. Taking advantage of a hunting trip, he went to Suruga province to see the princess. Although he tried to persuade her to come to the capital to be his consort, for some reason in her mind, the princess declined even this offer.

In the autumn of that year on the night in August when the whole sky was luminous with the pure light of the full moon, a fleecy white cloud came to meet Kaguya-hime and her father and from the summit of Fuji-no-yama they rose up to Heaven.

At that time she composed the following poem, which she attached to a potion of immortality and sent to the emperor.

"How I needs must don my spirit robe of light,
Yet in my heart, alas, I think of thee, dear Prince."

When the ruler read this poem, he was grieved and declared that he had no use for the potion of immortality. He ordered it to be taken to the summit of Fuji-no-yama, which was nearest Heaven, and to be burned. For a long time after that the summit of Fuji was burning. Its smoke was called the Smoke of Fuji, but legend says that it was the smoke from the burning potion that lingered there ever so long.

— *Kaidōki,* Maki 330, No. 130

48.   URIKOHIME

Long ago there was an old man and an old woman. The old man went to the mountains to cut wood and the old woman went to the river to wash clothes.

One day when the old woman went washing as usual at the river, a melon came floating down the stream. She picked it up and took it home to divide with her old man. When she cut it open, a very beautiful little girl was born. Because she was born from a melon, they named her Urikohime or Princess Melon. Little by little she grew up and at last she was a good daughter who wove at the loom day after day.

Thinking that they would take Uriko to the festival of the village shrine one year, the old man and the old woman went to town to buy a sedan chair for her. Uriko fastened the door tightly and wove at her loom in the house while they were gone.

An *ama-no-jaku* came along and disguising her voice, she said, "Open the door just a little for me."

Unsuspectingly Uriko opened the door a crack. Then the creature thrust a terrible hand through and opened the door with a clatter.

"I'll pick some persimmons for you from the garden behind the house," she said and led Uriko out into the back garden.

There she took off her clothes and tied her up to a tree. Putting on Urikohime's clothes, she then disguised herself like her and boldly sat down to weave.

Presently the old man and the old woman came home with the chair. "Now, Uriko, get into the chair," they said as they lifted the *ama-no-jaku* in and started away to the festival at the village shrine.

"Don't, don't let Uriko in the sedan chair!" the real Uriko cried from the shade of the persimmon tree in the back yard. "Only let the *ama-no-jaku* ride!"

When the old man and the old woman heard that voice, they were frightened and turned back. Then the old man swung his sickle and cut off the *ama-no-jaku's* head, which he threw into the millet patch.

The stalks of the millet turn red in Autumn because they were stained with the blood of the *ama-no-jaku*.

— Toshio Takagi, *Nippon Densetsu Shū*, p. 268
(Shimane)

49. TAKENOKO DŌJI

Long ago there was a young man named Sankichi who worked for a hooper. One day he went into the bamboo grove behind the shop to cut bamboo to use in making the hoops.

While he was working, he heard a voice call, "Sankichi!" He wondered who it could be.

It said, "Sankichi, I am here, I am here!"

Sankichi wondered, "Where is it?"

The voice replied, "I am here. I am in the bamboo."

Sankichi went over to the bamboo to see, but nobody was there. While he stood thinking it was all very strange, the voice said, "Please take me out of the bamboo, Sanchan."

Then Sankichi hurriedly sawed the bamboo and toppled it. Out came a tiny, tiny child. Sankichi was paralyzed with astonishment. Looking closely, he could see that it was a human being only five inches tall.

The little fellow said, "Thank you, Sanchan." His voice was comparatively big considering his size.

Sankichi decided to set him on the palm of his hand and talk to him. First of all, he wanted to know why he was inside the bamboo.

The little man said, "I was caught by a bad bamboo shoot and put inside the bamboo. That was why I could not go back to Heaven."

Sankichi asked, "How did you know my name?"

He replied, "I know everything in the world."

Sankichi asked, "What is your name?"

He answered, "My name is Takenoko Dōji, and I am 1,234 years old."

Then Sankichi asked, "Are you going back to Heaven right away?"

He answered, "I'm going back to Heaven right away, but if I don't repay your kindness before I go, I will be scolded by the Princess. I'll go back after I have rewarded you."

"If you are going to repay me," Sankichi said, "how will you do it?"

"I'll do seven things you like for you," he answered.

"Do you really mean it?" asked Sankichi. "You are not lying to me, are you?"

He said, "People from Heaven never lie." Then he taught Sankichi a magic formula to chant.

Sankichi had wanted for a long time to become a warrior. He repeated three times just as he was taught, "Takenoko, Takenoko, turn me into a warrior." Suddenly he turned into a real warrior.

Then Sankichi thanked Takenoko Dōji warmly and set out on a journey as a knight errant.

— *Mukashibanashi Kenkyū*, Vol. I, No. 8, p. 37
(Kuma-gun, Kumamoto)

50. KOMEBUKURO AND AWABUKURO

Long, long ago there were two girls, an older sister and a younger sister. The mother of Komebukuro, the older sister, was dead, and the mother of Awabukuro, the younger sister, was the new mother. The stepmother hated Komebukuro and abused her.

One day when the two sisters went with the village girls to gather chestnuts in the mountains, the older sister was given an old straw bag with a rotten bottom, and the younger sister was given a new straw bag. By evening all the other girls had filled their bags and wanted to start home, but Komebukuro's bag could never be filled because the bottom had come off.

All of her friends went home, leaving Komebukuro alone in the mountains. She was so hungry that she climbed down to a little stream to drink water. While she did this, a beautiful little white bird came flying toward her.

"Dear girl, I used to be your mother," it said. "You are gentle hearted and obey your present mother well. As a reward, I will give you this padded silk dress. Keep it hidden in the ground until something special happens, and then wear it as your best dress."

With the dress she also bestowed upon Komebukuro a flute made of hollyhock and a new straw bag. The girl soon filled the new bag to the brim and went back home in the night.

Four or five days after this there was a festival in a neighboring village. The stepmother dressed Awabukuro in a good dress and set out with her to see it.

When Komebukuro had said that she wanted to go, too, the stepmother said, "After you have spun three skeins of flax, you may come."

A crowd of Komebukuro's friends called for her while she was spinning the flax as fast as she could.

"My mother said that I had to do this work and I cannot go," she said.

Her friends felt sorry for her, and because they all helped, she finished her task much sooner than she had thought. Then she took out the silk dress which she had received from the little white bird. She put in on and set out looking quite beautiful with her friends.

As she went along the road blowing the hollyhock flute, the tune seemed to say,

"Whoever hears this little flute,
Birds in flight across the sky,
Rest your wings and listen;
Worms which crawl upon the ground,
Halt your feet and listen."

When they reached the shrine in the neighboring village to worship, they saw Awabukuro and her mother looking at the dancing dolls. Komebukuro peeled off the covering of a *manjū* and tossed it lightly at her younger sister, landing it on her cheek.

"Why, big sister threw a *manjū* covering at me from over there," she said.

The mother would not believe her. She said, "I made Komebukuro do work. How could she possibly be here by now?"

When the younger sister was looking the other way, after a little while Komebukuro tried throwing a strip of bamboo husk which had been wrapped around a piece of *ame* at her sister.

This, too, the younger sister told her mother.

"That is only somebody who looks like her," said her mother. "When somebody throws things at you, just turn away."

Presently it looked as though the mother and the younger sister were going to start home, so Komebukuro hurried back ahead of them. Changing her clothes, she looked as though nothing had happened.

On the next day somebody who said he wanted to marry Komebukuro came from the next village. The stepmother wanted him to marry Awabukuro instead. At last he decided that he would compare their looks and choose the one who was the prettier.

"What shall I put on my hair?" asked the younger sister while they were getting dressed.

Komebukuro and Awabukuro

The mother said to her, "Get the oil from the shelf and try rubbing it on."

When the older sister asked what she should use, the mother replied, "I don't care if you use the water from the kitchen."

The comb kept catching and snapping in the knots of Awabukuro's hair, which was kinky.

Her mother said, "It sounds just like the music of the *koto* or *shamisen* when it is plucked."

Komebukuro's hair was thick and smooth and the comb slipped through it easily.

The stepmother said with a sneer, "It sounds exactly like a foul snake gliding into its hole."

For all this, when their hair was combed, anyone could see that the older sister was far more beautiful, and Komebukuro was the one taken as a bride.

The younger sister was so jealous that she couldn't stand it. She teased her mother and said, "I want to ride right away in a beautiful sedan chair like that as a bride."

Nothing else would satisfy her, so the mother put Awabukuro onto a cart. Pulling it around, the mother called out at the top of her voice, "Anyone want a bride? Anyone want a bride?"

The cart tipped over and the girl fell into the rice paddy below, where she turned into a mud-snail. The bad stepmother fell into the water above the dam and turned into a sluice shellfish.

— Kunihiko Uchida, *Tsugaru Kōhi Shū*, p. 21
(Nanatsuishi, Ajigasawa-machi, Nishitsugaru-gun,
Aomori)

51. THE TREASURE-CLOAK OF THE *YAMA-UBA*

Long, long ago a beautiful only daughter lived out in the country in a region full of mountains. One summer day she went playing in the mountain with the people of the village. She strayed away from the rest and couldn't find her way back. It gradually grew dark and while she worried about which way to go, she saw a single light in the distance. Feeling quite happy, she went to the house and knocked. It proved to be the house of a *yama-uba* who was sitting alone, warming herself at the hearth.

"You've come thinking you could stay, I know, but this is a maneater's house, so I can't let you stop here," she said. "It would be better for you to look for an ordinary person's house."

The girl shuddered when she heard this, but she replied, "I don't care if you eat me up, if you will only let me stay. On a dark night like this, I would be sure to be eaten up by a bear or a wolf, anyway, if I am out on the mountain path. It would be much better to be eaten up here."

When the *yama-uba* heard this, she took pity on the girl and said, "In that case, I will give you my magic coat, although it is one of my greatest treasures. You had better wear this and go further on. If you put on this straw coat and repeat the words of the *Nyohō* three times, you can change into any form you choose, an old person or a little child. Furthermore, if you hold this coat and shake it, whatever you wish will come out." With these instructions she handed the coat to the girl.

The girl gladly accepted the coat and immediately turned herself into a tottering old woman. Then she left the house of the *yama-uba*.

Along her way dreadful demons gathered in ambush at one place.

One demon said, "Look, a woman is passing. How about catching her and eating her?"

Another demon answered, "Why eat a thin, dirty old woman like that?"

At last when it was about dawn, she came out into an un-known village and stood by a rich man's gate. "I am somebody with no place to go. A corner anywhere will do for me," she begged. "Please let me stay here."

When the kindhearted rich man heard this, he said, "Let her stay in a vacant place in the workers' house."

From that time she stayed in the long house. The days she spent spinning thread and doing such work, but in the evening, because she was bored, she would secretly change back to her real form and practice writing and such things when nobody was watching.

Late one night the rich man's son went outside and saw a single light burning in one room of the workers' house. He looked in and saw a beautiful girl quietly practicing brush writing all alone.

"I certainly want that girl for my bride," he thought.

The next day he looked all over the estate, but the girl was nowhere. While the young master was thinking there were strange things going on, one of the men who worked there happened to find her, also. He thought that she might be a ghost and told the master.

The rich man had the old lady called out immediately and pressed her with one proof after another. Finally the girl re-luctantly told about the treasure coat which she had received from the *yama-uba*. Taking off the coat, she changed back into the form of a girl and told in detail about her home and its place.

"Please take me back to my home," she said.

Through the rich man's power, they searched for the girl's home and soon found it. Her people thought that she had died by then and were holding a service for her. When the girl was sent back to them there was a great clamor and rejoicing.

Some time after that the girl went to the home of the rich man as a bride and the whole family prospered. *Medetashi. Medetashi.*

— Kendō Ishii, *Nippon Zenkoku Kokumin Dōwa*, p. 66
(Yamanashi)

52. THE OLD WOMAN'S SKIN

Long, long ago there was a father who owned many rice paddies. It was his custom to go every morning to tend to the water in the paddies, but one year dry weather lasted so long that the paddies dried up and were full of cracks in spite of his efforts.

There was a marsh near his paddies, however. One morning he walked around its margin and said to himself, "I have three daughters, but if somebody would just put water on my dry paddies, I would be willing to give him one of my daughters as a bride."

The next morning when he went to see his paddies, wasn't there water up to the very brim of those dry fields! The father thought it was terrible. It was something to be thankful for to have water on his paddies, but he realized that he would have to give one of his daughters to the snake who was the guardian spirit of the marsh. He worried and worried so much that he could not sleep that night. In the morning he did not have energy enough to get up.

His oldest daughter came to call him and said, "Father, are you going to keep on sleeping forever? Get up and eat!"

"I'm too worried," he answered. "I can't get any food down."

"What is it that worries you so much?" she asked.

"I have been going every morning to my rice paddies to see to the water, but they are always so dry that cracks have even appeared in the ground," he declared. "Yesterday morning while I walked around the edge of the marsh, I said to myself that I have three daughters and I would give one of them as a bride to anyone who would put water on my paddies. This morning when I went to see, there was water on them up to the brim. That's why I am worried. Would you be willing to go as a bride for me to the guardian spirit of the pond?"

The girl exclaimed, "There never was such a fool as our father!" She would not consent to her father's plea.

Then the second daughter came to call her father to breakfast. He tried telling her the same thing, but she refused to help him just as her sister had.

Finally the third daughter came to call her father. He told her what he had told the others and asked, "Would you go as a bride for me?"

"If it is something Father asks of me, I will obey," she replied. "But in return I want you to do as I say." What she wanted was to take with her as a bride a treasure for getting water, a thousand needles, and a treasure for getting fire.

At last the father was relieved. He got up and ate his breakfast.

The third daughter took her treasure that gets water, the treasure that gets fire, and the thousand needles and she set out on a horse to be the bride for the guardian spirit of the marsh. When she reached the marsh, she dismounted and threw the treasure that gets water into the water. Before her eyes the water disappeared. Next she flung the needles over the place. They stuck into the guardian of the marsh and he began to writhe and flounder around in pain. Then she tossed in the treasure that gets fire. The whole place began to burn until at last only the girl was left.

As she stood there blankly wondering what she should do, a frog came hopping up to her feet. "Young lady, young lady, why are you standing alone in such a place as this?" it asked.

The girl told the frog everything that had happened until then. "Do you know any place around here where I could find work?" she concluded.

The frog answered, "It is not safe for you to go dressed so beautifully. I will give you this *ubakawa,* an old woman's skin. Put it on and go over toward that village and see."

When the girl put on the old woman's skin, she suddenly turned into a stooped old woman. She went down the hill toward the village. "Here they might hire me," she thought as she stopped before a great mansion. "Even if it is only to sweep the yard, won't you please hire me?" she asked.

She was led before the master. "An old woman with a stooped back should be just right for sweeping the yard," he said and decided to give her work.

Everyone hustled around to fix a little room in the corner of the yard for the old woman and in a short time it was ready. Even if she was an old woman who was stooped over in the day time, at night she would go into her own little room and take off the old woman's skin, turning back into a beautiful girl. Then she would make a light and read a book.

One evening when the young master came home late from somewhere, he noticed a light in the old woman's room. Thinking this unusual, he peered in and saw a beautiful girl reading a book. This was strange, he thought, so the next evening he looked in again. Just as before there was a beautiful girl reading a book. Something queer was going on, he thought. The old woman who swept the yard might even be a fox or a badger and what should he do about it. But he could not forget the lovely girl and soon he could think of nothing else. He stopped eating and finally he became so ill he had to remain in bed.

Everyone in the household was worried. They took turns carrying trays to him and offering him food, but no matter who went, the young master would not even turn his head to look at them. In the meantime he grew weaker and weaker.

His father asked, "Isn't there somebody that appeals to my son? Is there anyone left in this house who has not taken a tray to him?"

His wife replied, "There is only the old woman who sweeps the yard."

"Well, then," he said, "try sending her to him with a tray!"

"Who would like food brought by an old woman like that?" declared his wife and would not agree.

"That's no way to talk," declared the master. "The thing to do is to try it."

Then when the old woman took off the skin and took a bath, she came out as her real self so beautiful she startled everyone.

For the first time the young master broke out into a laugh and ate the food. His father understood then that he loved the girl, and he gave them a splendid wedding.

After this that family prospered more and more.

— Yoshihiro Satō, Collector
(Fukuoka-machi, Ninohe-gun, Iwate)

53. THE WIFE LIKE A PICTURE

Long, long ago there was a young single man who had the reputation of being the poorest man on the island. It was said that his little house was only nine feet square. He had a little garden beside it, but he lived in such poverty that even if he had something to eat one day there might be nothing left to eat on the next.

He thought he would plant potatoes in his little garden and began spading it. Suddenly before him there stood a woman so beautiful that she surely must have descended from the upper world or have come floating up from the world below. As the young man stood staring blankly, the woman knelt upon the ground and pressing her hands together she said, "I beg of you to let me become your wife."

"I barely raise enough for me to live on alone," the young man protested, "and I do not have the strength to care for a beautiful person like you. You are so beautiful that you could marry a rich man with any amount of money so please do not think of being my wife and such things."

When he refused her, she said, "I will not marry anyone else in this whole world but you."

The young man was troubled and went straight home, but she followed right after him and began to clean up his dirty house.

When he said there was no rice to eat, she said, "Then I'll go and get some." She went out into the garden and sowed some seed. It sprouted immediately and before his eyes it ripened and in less than an hour she brought rice and cooked it for him.

In this way the woman cultivated the open fields and in less than no time he became a great land owner. Again, when the young man said his clothes were worn out, she raised silkworms, made thread and wove it to make him clothes. Since the house was small, a big one made of wood was built and a storehouse, too. The young man was soon numbered among the few men of great wealth in the village.

The man would continue to go to his garden patch to work every day, but would come home again immediately.

His wife asked one day, "When you used to have such a reputation for being a good worker, why do you come back home right away these days?"

He replied, "When I can't see your face for even one hour, I get so I can no longer work."

"If that is it, I have the right thing for you," she said. "Take this with you now." She pulled out a picture of herself and handed it to her husband.

The man set up a post in his garden and fastened his wife's picture onto it. Every now and then he would stop and look at it and then go on with his work. In the meantime a strong wind blew up and carried the picture off somewhere. He went home dejectedly and told his wife what had happened. She got out a new picture and handed it to her husband.

On the other hand, the picture that blew away went whirling up in the sky and then fell onto the veranda of the feudal lord's mansion. The one who found it was the feudal lord. After he had admired it for some time he turned to his men and said, "There cannot actually be such a beautiful woman in this world, can there."

They all agreed that since it was a picture it was that beautiful. One of them, however, came forward and looked intently at the picture and declared, "It happens that there is just such a woman. Her house is about five miles from here and she is the wife of that man who used to be so poor. She came from somewhere to be his bride, after which that family built a great mansion and expanded until at present it is the second or third wealthiest in the village. If this woman pleases you as much as that, you have a right to summon her to you," he concluded.

The feudal lord considered the matter for a while and then announced, "I agree!" Accordingly he sent an order to the man's house. "You bring two wrestlers and come to me and I will hire two men," it said. "If yours win in a wrestling match, I will pay you five hundred *ryō*. If your men lose, you send your wife to me."

The husband shed tears and felt miserable about the problem, but his wife said, "Do not worry in the least about this. I will go and hire wrestlers." She had barely left when she returned bringing two old men, one seventy years old and the other eighty.

When her husband saw them he burst into tears and cried, "How can such old men wrestle! This is where you and I must part and I must live without you."

"Don't worry," she replied. "Take them to the wrestling match."

He set out with them to the feudal lord's place and there he found two wrestlers as big as sixteen gallon barrels. The great crowd of retainers who had gathered to see the match tittered when they saw the two old men the husband brought.

To begin with, a terribly huge wrestler came out from the feudal lord's side and stamped into the ring. Then from the man's side the seventy year old came forth. The match had barely started when the old man threw the wrestler as big as a barrel out of the ring and drove him about a foot into the ground. Next, the eighty year old man came out and thrust his opponent two feet into the ground. Since the feudal lord lost, the man received the five hundred *ryō* according to the agreement and went home full of fresh vigor and delight. He gave each of the old men one hundred *ryō* and sent them away.

After this was done, his wife said, "Now my duty is finished. I would like to be permitted to leave from this day."

The startled man exclaimed, "Why do you suddenly say a thing like that. If it means I must part from you, I want to die." He grasped his wife by the hand and sighed.

"You shouldn't say such a thing," she answered. "Well, then, I'll give you just the hand you are clinging to." With that she cut off her hand and went away somewhere.

That night the man had difficulty in getting to sleep because he was thinking so much about his wife and in the morning he quite overslept. When he awoke he stared vacantly around the house in which he was all alone. He heard voices of people passing. There was a shrine behind the man's house and the people were returning from worshipping there.

He heard somebody say, "Strange, isn't it, that the two male deities each has a hundred *ryō* hanging from his neck and the female deity in the middle has one hand cut off. Just what do you suppose is the reason for that."

The man leaped up with astonishment. Could it be that

who he thought was his wife was really a goddess? What a pity. He hurriedly took the hand from the day before and went to the shrine. Yes, the female deity was missing one hand.

"I did not know you were a goddess," he said respectfully. "I hardly know what to say."

He laid the hand before her and worshipped with bowed head. Presently he lifted his face and looked. The hand of the goddess was fastened on perfectly where it had been formerly.

The goddess had helped him because he was an honest man.

— *Mukashibanashi Kenkyū,* Vol. II, No. 2, p. 46
(Nase, Amami Ōshima, Kagoshima)

54. THE ORIGIN OF THE GOD OF THE KITCHEN HEARTH

Long ago there was a farmer in a certain village. He was overtaken by a sudden shower one evening when he was coming home from a trip, and he took refuge for some time in the grove of Dōrokujin by the side of the road.

There was a man passing by the grove on horseback who called in the dark. "Are you in, Dōrokujin? There are to be two confinements at the village tonight. Let's go together and read the fortunes of the babies born."

"Thanks for coming by to invite me," a voice from the grove replied, "but just now I have a guest who has taken shelter from the rain, and I can't get away. I leave it to you."

"Then I'll go on alone," the first voice said, and the hoof beats of the horse went off in the distance.

Now this village happened to be that farmer's village, and thinking it was a bit strange, he was all ears.

In a short time the man on the horse returned and again from the front the voice of somebody passing called, "At the main family it was a boy and in the branch family it was a girl. The girl's luck is good, but the boy has no luck. If they are married, the couple's luck will flourish on the strength of the wife's luck."

By a mere chance the farmer had overheard the forecast of the fortunes of the children born that day. Hurrying home to his village, he found that a boy baby had been born at his house and a girl at the branch family next door. He was completely taken by surprise. He immediately talked it over with his neighbor, and the two decided to contract a wedding settlement then and there.

When the two children grew up, they married and sure enough their household became more and more prosperous. But the husband could not bear to think this was because of his wife's good fortune. After a while he began to find fault with everything she did. Finally he cooked red rice and tied it onto a red cow. He then put his wife on the cow and after leading it off to a distant meadow, he turned it loose and chased it away.

Crying as she rode the red cow, the wife let it carry her wherever it wanted to. It went gradually into the mountains and finally came to a stop in front of a solitary cottage far back in the mountains.

The kind hearted man who owned the house helped the woman in many ways. Since she had no place to go, she stayed there and finally became his wife. After that the fortunes of this house visibly mended. Eventually they lived in perfect comfort and employed many men and women.

From exactly the same time the house which had turned out the wife had nothing but loss. At last the man's fortune was totally wrecked and he lost even the fields which he had inherited from his forefathers. Completely ruined, he turned to selling bamboo baskets.

As the basket seller went about here and there with his wares, he happened to come across a splendid house standing by itself far back in the mountains. He got the people there to buy all of his baskets. After that, since he could not sell them anywhere else, he would go almost every day to that one house in the mountains and get them to buy his baskets.

One day the wife at the house looked at the face of the basket seller intently and exclaimed, "Why have you fallen so low? Have you forgotten even what your former wife looks like?"

For the first time the basket seller recognized in the woman of the house his former wife, whom he had put on the red cow and driven away the year before. He was so stunned that he fell foaming at the mouth and died.

The wife took pity on him when she saw this. Before anyone could find out, she buried his corpse in the dirt floor behind the cook stove. Then with her own hands she made *bota-mochi,* which she gave as an offering.

When her family and workers came home, she said, "I have set up Kōjin Sama, God of the Kitchen Hearth, behind the stove today. I made this *bota-mochi* to celebrate. Eat as much as you want."

That was the beginning, and even now at farm houses *bota-mochi* is made for the festival of the God of the Kitchen Hearth.

— Kunihiko Uchida, *Nansō no Rizoku*
(Chōsei-gun, Chiba)

55. THE DRIFTLOG GOD

Once upon a time there was a man who liked to fish. He got up one morning at dawn and set out, but because it was too early, he had to wait for the tide. Using a driftlog which had rolled up to the beach as a pillow, he dozed for a while. In the midst of the sound of the waves he heard a voice calling somebody.

The voice said, "Mr. Driftlog, Mr. Driftlog, there has been a birth in the village near here so come along to settle the fortune."

The driftlog which was being used as a pillow replied, "I have the bad luck of being used as a pillow by a man now and I can't move. Although it will be inconvenient for you, please go alone today."

Hearing this the fisherman thought there were strange things going on. Presently he heard the former voice again.

"I'm back now," the voice said.

"That was good of you," the log answered. "How was the birth and how did the fortune turn out?"

"A little girl was born," came the reply. "When she is eighteen, she will meet with danger from water, but if she escapes from this evil fortune, she will be blessed with a fortune that will fill seven storehouses."

This was stranger and stranger thought the man, but he went ahead and fished. When he went home, he found that a little girl had been born unexpectedly in his family. Recalling the talk of the driftlog on the beach that morning, he was astonished and wondered if it could have concerned his child. He was full of uneasiness but he did not disclose it to anybody.

Days and months passed until during the spring when his daughter would be eighteen. It was settled that she would go as a bride to the next village.

On the night before the wedding, without telling anyone, the father kept in mind what he had heard by the driftlog. He set out a sedge hat and cloak to use in case of rain. The next day was bright and clear, but in spite of the custom at that village for the father not to go along at such a time, the man took the rain things and accompanied his daughter. Sure enough, on their way it suddenly began to rain. Stopping his daughter from taking shelter below a rocky cliff, he put the rain hat and cloak onto her and hurried her to the neighboring village safely. There the wedding ceremony was performed.

On the following day when those who had accompanied the bride were returning, they passed the previous cliff where the girl had wanted to take shelter. The cliff had crumbled and fallen.

Thanks to her father, the girl's life had been saved, and after that she really had a happy life as rich as seven full storehouses.

— Sumako Osada, Collector
(Amami Ōshima, Kagoshima)

56. YASUKE OF YAMURA

Long ago there was a young farmer named Yasuke who was a faithful son at Yamura in Shinshū. Although he was honest and hard-working, the home was poor.

One year he set out with only a little money to buy things for New Year's at the year's-end market. On the way he found a copper pheasant fluttering in a snare by the side of the road. "I must save it," he thought and loosened the cords of the net and set the pheasant free. He decided that it was not fair to the owner of the snare just to set the bird free, so he fastened the string of cash which he held in his hand to the net in exchange for the bird. Since he could no longer do any shopping, he went back empty handed.

His mother, who was a kindhearted woman, said that he had done a good thing. The mother and son then spent a bleak New Year's Day with nothing to eat.

Now an unfamiliar young woman called at the house saying, "I am a traveler. I am cut off by the snow and in difficulty. If you would only let me stay here until spring, I would be willing to do any kind of work."

She did all kinds of work around the house for the mother. She was, indeed, a gentle, beautiful young woman.

One day Yasuke's mother talked things over with her and said, "If you have no parents and relatives, wouldn't you rather stay here and be my son's bride?"

The girl gladly agreed and married him.

For some years they lived together happily. Then a terrible demon began to haunt Ariake-yama. Tamura Shōgun received orders from the Imperial Court to go to destroy it. Because Yasuke of Yamura was skillful with the bow, he had to accompany Tamura Shōgun in the attack upon the demon.

At that time Yasuke's wife called him quietly and talked with him. "The demon at Ariake-yama is called Gishi-ki," she said. "You can never bring him down with an ordinary arrow. If you shoot him with an arrow feathered with the feathers with thirteen bands from the tail of the copper pheasant, you can shoot him down with a single arrow. Because it is the greatest task which a man can do in his life, I will give you those feathers. I am the bird which was caught in the snare, which you saved long ago at the close of the year."

So saying she flew away crying. Yasuke saw that she had left behind the wonderful tail feathers with thirteen bands.

That is why the demon at Ariake-yama was subdued and the Japanese Alps became pleasant mountains. It was solely due to the feat of Yasuke. He was richly rewarded for his exploit, and his fame has lasted long in the mountains of Shinshū.

— *Minamiazumi-gun Shi*, p. 927
(Minamiazumi-gun, Nagano)

57. THE FOX WIFE

Long ago there was a man named Saburobē at Mangyō in Noto province. When he went to the privy one night and came back, he found two wives in his room. One or the other had to be a goblin, but there was absolutely not a hair's difference in their appearance nor in what they said. He tried all kinds of puzzles for them to solve, but they both answered everything easily and he didn't know what to do. At last, since there was a slight doubt about one, she was driven out and the other was allowed to stay in the house.

The house began to do well after that, and even two sons were born. When the two children had grown a little bigger, they played hide-and-seek at their house one day. By chance they discovered that their mother had a tail. She could no longer remain because they found out what she really was.

"The truth is that I was a fox," she said, and leaving her two children behind, she ran away crying.

After that when the time came for the rice grains to form every year, the fox-wife would walk around Saburobē's rice field and chant, "Be fruitful, but hide the ears."

And when the rice assessors would come to see, they would always excuse this family from payments because the rice grains at that house alone never seemed to fill in well. However, when the rice was harvested and brought into the house to thresh, there would always be a greater harvest than at any other house, and the family became richer and richer.

— *Kashima-gun Shi,* p. 978
(Kashima-gun, Ishikawa)

58. THE FROG WIFE

Once upon a time there was a man living with his mother. One day when he went into the hills, he found a snake starting to swallow a frog. When he saw this, he killed the snake and set the frog free. It looked very happy and hurried away.

Four or five days after this happened, while the man was eating supper in the evening with his mother after returning from the hills, a beautiful girl called at their home. She begged them to let her stay with them as his bride. Since the young man was getting around the age to marry, they decided they might as well ask her to be his bride and so it was settled that she should marry him. The girl was a good worker and she seemed to be able to do anything. It was strange, however, that she never appeared to eat a single morsel of food. She would go to the little pond in the yard and sip up some water, *pechapecha pechapecha*, and then go back to work full of life.

After some days had passed this way, she said, "It is rather hard for me to say, but today there is to be a memorial service at my parents' home. Please let me go back for the day."

"That's all right," said the man generously. "Go by all means." But since he did not know exactly what sort of family she had come from, he decided to follow his bride without letting her know.

She went off quickly toward a big pond fairly far back in the hills. Suddenly she jumped into it with a splash.

"Ah ha, so she's a frog," concluded the young man, aware of it for the first time.

Then as though it was about time for the memorial service to start in the pond, a big frog leaped onto a pile that was standing in the middle of the pond and exactly in front of the man. Many small frogs then came jumping up out of the water onto piles standing around it.

Presently the big frog sounded forth with, "*Gyaashin, gyaashin, gyaashin, gyaashin.*" All the little frogs joined their voices in a response, "*Gyashi, gyashi, gyashi, gyashi.*" It sounded all the world like sutras being chanted as they continued.

All this amused the man, who was listening, until he could hardly stand it. Thinking he would surprise them with a little prank, he picked up a big stone and tossed it into the center of the pond. At that all the many frogs went jumping back into the pond, *pocha, pocha, pocha, pocha.* After seeing this, the man went home.

The next day the bride came back home announcing, "I have come back now."

The old woman asked, "How was it? Was there a fine memorial service?"

"It really was a fine service," the girl replied, "but right while everybody was joining in the sutra, a big rock came falling from the roof and put an end to everything. It was no time for a sutra, but terribly, terribly scarey. We gave up right in the midst of it."

"Well, that was really too bad," remarked the old woman.

In the meantime, the bride went off somewhere.

— Hisako Maruyama, Collector
(Hatano-mura, Sado-gun, Niigata)

59. THE SNAKE'S TREASURE

Long ago a beautiful young girl used to go every day to worship at Miidera, a temple in the Province of Ōmi. She would always stop at a certain teahouse by the lake to rest. The son of a neighboring wine merchant noticed her and thought he would like to marry her. He asked the old woman at the teahouse to tell the girl for him. The girl said that she was going to the temple for one hundred days because she was making a special petition. If it would be all right to wait until that was finished, she would marry him. The young man thought there was no reason to object, so the talk was carried out and the time approached for the wedding.

Finally the day came. Although the weather had been clear until then, when the hour arrived, it suddenly began to rain.

Presently it stopped and the girl arrived bringing her wedding outfit and furnishings.

From that time the wine merchant's family suddenly began to prosper. In a short time the bride became pregnant. She asked her mother-in-law to lend her one of the storehouses and she began sleeping in it. As the day grew near for her baby to be born, she said over and over, "While I am giving birth to my child, please do not let anybody look into the storehouse."

However, when the time came and the young man thought of how his wife was suffering, he was beside himself with worry. Unconsciously he broke the agreement and peered into the storehouse, only to be dumbfounded. There was a huge snake lying across the floor almost filling the room. It had a baby placed near the middle of its body as though it was holding it in its arms. And wasn't it licking the baby with its tongue! The young man was so stunned he could not move.

Aware that she had been seen in that form, the snake changed back into her human form and came out of the storehouse. She said, "Since this has happened, I can no longer stay here. I want permission to go home." Then, thinking about her little son, she added, "After I am gone, I am sure you will have trouble because there will be no milk for the baby. I will take out one of my eyes and leave it. Bring him up by letting him suck on it. If anything happens that you need me, come to the shore of the lake and call." Saying this, she laid her eye there and went off somewhere before anybody knew.

After that, the child's hunger was always satisfied when they let him suck the eyeball. One day the feudal lord heard about this strange treasure. He had it seized and brought for his own child. At the wine merchant's house the baby cried so much that they did not know what to do or where to turn for help. Then they remembered the words of the mother when she left the house.

The father went to the shore of the lake and called her.

The woman appeared from out of the water. When she heard the story of what had happened, she said, "Well, then—," and scooped out her remaining eye. As she handed it to the father she declared, "With this, both of my eyes are lost and I can no longer see the world. I have given up the happiness of seeing this child of mine as he grows up. When he is bigger, please make him bell ringer at Miidera. With that sound I can know when it is morning and evening as long as I live." When she finished speaking, she returned to the water and disappeared.

The child grew up with the help of that treasure and he became the bell ringer at Miidera according to his mother's wish.

— Toshio Iwasaki, *Iwaki Mukashibanashi Shū*, p. 8
(Taira-shi, Fukushima)

60. MONEY TO THE OLD MAN

This is a story of how a man suddenly became rich by just standing absent-mindedly and letting gold and silver come flying.

Long ago there lived a good old man and a bad old man in a village. Once when the good old man went into the mountains alone to work, he heard voices calling from somewhere.

Voices repeated over and over, "Shall we hold fast to you or stick fast to you?"

Finally the old man thoughtlessly answered, "If you're going to hold fast, hold fast! If you're going to stick fast, stick fast!"

Immediately lumps of gold and silver came flying and landed on his shoulders and back until it made him grunt.

He carried all this home and spread it out in the house. While he and his old woman were gazing at it together, the bad old man came over from next door and became envious.

He said "I want to do that, too, and bring home treasure on my back."

He set out the next day into the same mountains. Just as he had expected, voices came calling from both sides of the mountain.

They called, "Shall we stick fast to you or hold fast to you?"

In great glee, the bad old man answered, "If you're going to stick fast, stick fast! If you're going to hold fast, hold fast!"

This time pitch came flying down from the tops of the pine trees and landed on the old man's shoulders and back until he was heavily loaded.

"Granny, Granny, I'm home!" he called. "Hurry! bring a light and let's see!"

His old woman brought the light, but it came so close that the pitch caught on fire, burning the old man badly.

— Seiichi Moriguchi, *Kii Arita-gun Dōwa-shū*, p. 11
(Arita-gun, Wakayama)

61. THE FIRE FOR NEW YEAR'S EVE

Long, long ago there was a poor pack-horse leader who lived in the country. The next day was to be New Year's Day, but since there was no work, he started home without a load on his horse. He suddenly noticed a dirty beggar who had fallen down and was groaning in the shade of the pine trees that lined the highway.

"Dear me! Can there be men worse off than I?" he thought. "I must help this man."

Fortunately the rack was empty, so he loaded the beggar onto his horse and took him home. Then he and his wife talked it over. They decided to spread out a straw mat on the dirt floor. They laid the beggar down on it carefully and covered him with straw matting. They had nothing for him to eat, but they built a good fire on the hearth beside him and then let him pass New Year's Eve as best he could.

On New Year's Day the sun had risen high, but the beggar did not get up and come out. The man and his wife went in by him and tried to call him. There was no answer. It seemed to them that he had turned cold and they were terribly worried. They pulled off the piece of straw matting with which they had covered him and found that what they had thought was a beggar was a great lump of gold.

The pack-horse leader made use of the gold and immediately became known as a rich man.

— *Tabi to Densetsu*, Vol. IV, No. 4, p. 60
(Minamishidara-gun, Aichi)

62. THE TOAD THAT TALKED

Once upon a time when an old man was walking through a thicket, he found a snake about to swallow a toad. Feeling sorry for the toad, he rescued it and took it home with him.

The toad spoke like a human being when this happened and thanked the old man. He told the old man to take him to town and let him sing to earn money.

The old man did as he was told and took the toad with him to town the next day. "A toad that talks, a toad that talks," he called as he went along until a great crowd of curious people gathered. When he made the toad sing, it did very well and sang whatever was requested. He was such an attraction that the old man made more money than he had ever dreamed of.

An old neighbor, who was a bad man, thought he would like to try earning some himself. He insisted on borrowing the toad and taking it to town to make it sing in the same way, but the toad refused to sing anything. The people who had gathered to hear grew angry and beat up the neighbor.

Enraged over this treatment, the old man declared, "This is all the toad's fault, the spiteful little beast!" Then he killed it.

The good old man felt badly about this. He asked for half of its flesh which he brought home, and buried in front of his porch. In the night a Judas tree sprouted and suddenly it spread out, winding around the house several times. There was the sound of clinking metal, *chin kuwararin, chin kuwararin.* In the morning when the old man opened his doors, what piles of gold and silver coins he found around his house, almost burying it!

When the neighbor saw that, he thought he would try once more to imitate him. He took the remaining flesh of the frog and buried it in front of his own porch. Just as before, a Judas tree sprouted in the night and grew thick, enfolding the house. He could not wait until dawn and striking a light, he went out to see. All around the house there had fallen heaps of cow dung.

— *Kyōdo Kenkyū,* Vol. V. No. 4, p. 49
(Amakusa-gun, Kumamoto)

63. THE JIZŌ WITH SEDGE HATS

Long, long ago there lived a well-meaning old man and his wife in a village. The old man made a living by making sedge hats every day and taking them to town to sell.

On the day before New Year's he went out to sell them as usual, but nobody would buy a single hat at the market for the year's end. Giving up, he loaded the hats on his back and started home.

A snow storm came up, and the Jizō images in the middle of the field looked cold and wet.

"This is too bad," thought the old man. He put his six sedge hats on the heads of the six Jizō images.

When he got home, he told his wife what he had done. Since there was nothing else to do, they went to sleep.

As the dawn of the New Year was approaching, the sound of sleds could be heard in the distance and voices singing,

"Who put on the six Jizō
The six hats of sedge?
Where's that Grandpa's house?
Where's that Grandma's house?"

The singing voices of those drawing the sleds drew nearer and nearer. The old man and the old woman jumped up and ran to the door calling, "Here we are! Here we are!"

Lots of bags of treasures had been tossed in a heap on the door step, and the backs of the six Jizō images could be seen departing.

— Kizen Sasaki, *Esashi-gun Mukashibanashi*, p. 4
(Esashi-gun, Iwate)

64. THE GHOSTS OF COINS

Once upon a time there was an old man and an old woman living in a certain place. Although they toiled away year in and year out, wearing their coarse working clothes, they never reached a time when they could have any ease in life. Even if they did not get to be as rich as any particular *chōja*, they wished at least they could be as rich as some in the village and have a good life every day.

Thus the end of another year approached. Every year the old man was in the habit of going in the direction of blessing according to the almanac to pray for good fortune in the New Year. Thinking he would make a special petition to the deity for prosperity for this coming year, the old man ate his New Year's Eve noodles, and waiting for the last of the strokes of the temple bell, he dressed in his best clothes and set out for the shrine of Ujigami Sama, his tutelary god, before anybody else.

"Although I have always come this way each year to pray, why is it no good fortune ever comes my way? Please, this year, let us have at least enough to eat without having to toil and sweat so much for it," he prayed with his hands pressed reverently together before him.

As he did this, he heard the voice of the deity. It declared, "Indeed, it is exactly as you say. Well, tonight there will be a feudal procession passing your house. Wait up for it without sleeping, and try striking the leader at the head of the procession."

The old man went home delighted and waited for night to come. At last toward midnight he could hear sounds approaching from the distance. As they came nearer he could hear the shouts and clatter of a procession of samurai on horses. When he looked out to see who was riding at the head, he saw a splendid samurai in ceremonial regalia, a gold sword at his side. He sat astride his horse with great poise.

"Oh, so this is it! I must strike him, must I," he thought to himself. But the samurai was so splendid that he was too frightened to go out to him. While he was hesitating and holding back, the procession passed completely by.

Presently, however, another procession on horseback came along. A splendid samurai dressed in the same way with a silver sword at his side was riding a white horse at the head of the procession.

"This time I'll certainly strike him," resolved the old man. He thought, "Shall I go out now? Now, shall I go out?"

In the meantime he lost his nerve at the appearance of the samurai and could not bring himself to strike him.

"There, I've lost my chance. The second fellows have already gone, but I'll strike the next ones that come no matter what happens," he said as he waited.

This time there was no sound of bells on bridles but only a strange clumping noise, *hyokosuka, hyokosuka,* approaching.

"There don't seem to be any horses this time," he said as he looked out.

A crowd of one-eyed, crippled low-class samurai came hobbling along.

"Well, if they are this sort, I can strike them all I want," he thought as he went leaping out of his house and gave the leader a resounding whack.

With a clatter, *chara, chara, charaan,* the whole crowd disappeared. The old man called his wife to bring a light and he looked around. Only two or three one-*mon* coins had fallen on the ground.

"What's this," he scolded. "This doesn't amount to anything." He returned to Ujigami Sama to complain.

He heard the voice of the deity once more. It said, "If you had struck the leader of the first procession, you would have gained three thousand *ryō.* Even if you had struck the second, you would have had one thousand *ryō.* Because you only struck the one-eyed, crippled leader of the last one, you received two or three *mon.* It looks like you two have no good fortune coming your way. You had better give up trying to become rich."

— Hiroko Ikeda, Collector
(Ebi-mura, now Kōfu-machi, Hino-gun, Tottori)

65. THE FORBIDDEN ROOM

Once upon a time a good old man and a bad old man lived as neighbors. One day while the good old man was cutting a big tree, a beautiful girl came out and said, "Old man, old man, please do not cut that tree down. If you cut it down, I will lose my place to live. Instead of doing that, please come to my house for a little while."

Led by the girl, the old man went to her house. In front there was a beautiful stream of clear water which had the scent of wine.

While he was thinking how good he felt, the girl dipped up some of the water into a basin, saying, "Here, wash your feet in this and then come in."

He went inside. She served him delicious wine and fish and other good things. Then she said, "Old man, old man, let me show you my rooms. Please come this way."

She led him further into the house. "This is the New Year's room," she said and showed him pine and bamboo trees hung with a sacred rope. In the room for the Second Month there were plum, peach, and cherry trees in full bloom. In the room for the Third Month there were dolls arranged for the Doll Festival. She showed him all the rooms through the Twelfth Month.

Then the girl said, "Old man, I must go to town to shop now and I will leave the key with you. You may look into any room you wish, but please do not look into the room for the Second Month."

After saying this, she went out.

The old man followed her instructions and looked freely into all the rooms except for the one for the Second Month. Then he went out to where the clear stream was flowing. He dipped up some of the wine and brought it inside to drink while he kept watch of the house.

Soon the beautiful girl returned. She said, "I have nothing nice to give you as a gift, but I bought this wooden ladle. When you want to cook rice, put water into a kettle and set it on the fire. Then as you stir it with this ladle, if you say, 'Boil rice, boil rice,' you can have cooked rice. You can make soup or fish soup or anything else you want in the same way. If you just do as I say, it will happen according to your wish."

She gave him the ladle and said, "Now it is getting late and your old woman will be worrying. Hurry on home."

The old man thanked her and went home. He told his wife all that had happened that day. They promptly filled a kettle with water and set it on the fire and did as he was told.

Since they could cook rice and soup and anything they wanted, they were eating very happily when the bad old woman from next door came and said she wanted to borrow some live coals to start her fire.

"We will give you the fire," they said, "but at least stay for a bowl of fish soup."

As she accepted their offer, the old woman asked, "What's going on today that you are having such good things to eat?"

The old man told her about going into the hills to cut a tree and how the beautiful girl came out and led him away.

The bad old woman went right home and insisted that her old man go to the hills although he did not want to go at all.

While this old man was doing as his neighbor had done, the beautiful girl led him away and asked him to look after her house while she left. In the same way, she told him very firmly not to look into the room for the Second Month.

The bad old man did not follow her instructions. When he opened the door for the Second Month, a nightingale came flying out, crying, *"Hoo-hokekyo."*

Suddenly the place was once more at the base of the big tree in the mountains.

— Tayoko Noda, *Tekkiri Anesama*, p. 200
(Gonohe-machi, Sannohe-gun, Aomori)

66. RAT PARADISE

Long, long ago an old man and an old woman lived very happily together. Every day the old man went to the hills behind their home to cut wood and the old woman stayed at home to work and look after the house.

On this day the old man set out briskly as usual, his ax hung at his side, while it was still dark. At about midday, the old woman made some of the old man's favorite dumplings, put them into a lunch box, and set out with them to the hills behind the house.

When she got as far as the pass, she happened to stumble on a rock and fall. The lid to the box was jolted off and a dumpling fell out and started rolling off. Forgetting how tired she was, the old woman chased the dumpling calling, "Wait, dumpling! Wait, dumpling!" Try as she would, she could not catch up with it.

In the meantime the dumpling dropped into a hole. Still calling, "Wait, dumpling! Wait, dumpling!" the old woman followed it into the hole, but inside it was pitch dark and she lost sight of it. While she was hesitating about which direction to take, she heard voices further inside singing lustily and keeping time as they pounded on a mortar, *ton ton totton, totto koton.* With fear and trembling she peered ahead. She saw a great crowd of huge rats pounding away at a mortar with all their might, singing:

"If only cats would pass on by
The Paradise of Rats,
The world would fill with bliss.
Yasshishi, yasshishi."

The old woman tried not to burst out laughing and let out a "meow" like a stray cat.

At that the rats started scrambling away frantically and shrieking, "That stray cat is here again. Run! Let's run!" In an instant they had run off and hid.

When the old woman came up to look, she found the mortar was made of gold and so was the pestle! Besides, all kinds of treasures heaped as high as a mountain were there. She gathered them all up and packing them on her back, she went home very happy.

The old man, too, came home and the two of them prepared to pound rice. When they put a single grain of rice in the mortar and pounded it, suddenly the mortar would be filled to overflowing. In this way the good old man and woman gradually became rich.

Next door there lived a greedy old woman who could not bear to see this going on. She hurriedly sent her old man off to the hills to work while she made dumplings and followed later. When she had nearly arrived at the pass which she had made sure of in advance, she took out a dumpling and rolled it down the hill. Then she chased it calling, "Wait, dumpling, wait dumpling!" until it went into a dark hole.

She went stealthily after it into the hole, tiptoeing far inside and peered around. Today, too, the rats had gathered and were absorbed in pounding in the mortar, *totto-ko totto-ko, ton, ton,* and singing:

> "If only cats would pass on by
> The Paradise of Rats,
> The world would fill with bliss.
> *Yasshishi, yasshishi.*"

The old woman, eager to take a chance, yelled, "Meow!"

She thought that the rats would run off at that, but instead, they all looked around fiercely and cried, "That's the greedy old woman who came before. Let's pound her up!"

They cut off her hands and feet and all together they threw her into the mortar and pounded her to death.

— Fukuoka-ken Mukashibanashi Shū, No. 156
(Kiku-gun, Fukuoka)

67. THE HIDDEN VILLAGE

This is what really happened long ago on our island Kikai-jima.

There is a great cliff near the beach by Tenju Port at Shidooke. A certain man always took his cow there to stake it out. One day after he had tied it up as usual, he felt so sleepy that he fell sound asleep. When he woke up presently and looked around, what a sight met his eyes. A countless number of ants had swarmed out, pulled his big cow over, and were starting to drag it through an opening in the cliff. This certainly wouldn't do. The man pulled the rope with all his might, but he could not draw the cow back. Instead, he was dragged along with it into the cave. Strangely enough, inside the cave was a big meadow and there were broad patches of garden.

A solitary man who was there said to the fellow, "I certainly am thankful. The soil in my garden was so hard I couldn't plow it, but with the help of your cow I could do it."

The astonished fellow declared, "I'll give you my cow, but please spare my life!"

"No, no, there is no reason to be afraid," replied the man. He paid the owner a lot of money instead. But he asked him not to tell anyone what had happened. He said, "Any time you need money, always come here for some."

Suddenly the owner of the cow became a wealthy man. People are likely to be careless, however, so when he became so rich he could spend freely, he forgot his pledge. One day when he was drunk he said to his friends, "I have no worry about money!" Then he told them what had happened the other day.

His friends said they did not want any money, but they asked him to take them to see the place. They went with him to the cliff by the beach, but this time the entrance to the cave was closed and he could not get it open any more.

That was not all. The man's money was gradually spent and once more he became a poor man.

— Ichirō Iwakura, *Kikaijima Mukashibanashi Shū*, p. 125
(Kikaijima, Ōshima-gun, Kagoshima)

68. DUMPLING PARADISE

Long, long ago there was an old man and an old woman in a certain place. While they were making dumplings for the Festival of Spirits one spring, one dumpling dropped to the floor and went rolling away.

"Dumpling, dumpling, how far are you rolling?" cried the old man as he ran after it.

"I'll roll to Jizō San's cave," it answered, finally rolling right into the cave.

The old man went into the cave, too, and found that the bottom of the cave was wide. A Jizō was standing there. The old man managed to catch the dumpling just as it came to a stop in front of the Jizō image. The part of the dumpling that had dirt on it the old man ate himself, and he gave the part without dirt on it to Jizō.

In the meantime it began to grow dark. The old man thought that he had better go home.

"Climb up onto my lap," said Jizō.

"It would not be right. I can't climb up," answered the old man.

"It's all right. Climb up," insisted Jizō.

The old man climbed up as he was told.

"Now climb onto my shoulders," said the image then.

"I have already climbed up as far as your lap, and I don't dare to climb up any higher," refused the old man.

"But climb up anyway," insisted Jizō.

The old man climbed up to his shoulders.

"Now climb onto my head," the image then said.

He did his best to refuse, but Jizō insisted that he climb up, so the old man gave in and climbed onto his head.

Then Jizō lent his fan to the old man. "Presently the demons will gather here and begin to gamble," said the image. "At the right time, beat this fan and imitate a rooster's crow."

Sure enough, a crowd of demons came along and began gambling. After a while the old man did as Jizō had told him, imitating the rooster's crow.

117

"There, it's dawn already," the demons cried and rushed out with a shout, leaving the old coins and gold there as they ran off somewhere.

The old man received all the coins and gold from Jizō and took them home in high glee. His old woman was waiting for him. Together they spread out all the coins and gold pieces, looking at them in delight.

Just then the old woman from next door came to call. When she asked why the folks at that house looked so happy, the honest old man told her exactly what had happened.

"Then I'm going to send my old man to Jizō's cave, too, I am," she declared, hurrying home.

The two neighbors then hastily started making dumplings. They took one out into the yard and dropped it, but because it would not move, the old man kicked it along. He kept at it until he got it into the cave. Then he followed it in quite boldly. Going over before the Jizō image, he found the dumpling lying all covered with dirt. The bad old man took out the inside which was still clean and ate it, giving the dirty outside part to Jizō.

Since nobody invited him to climb up, he climbed up to Jizō's lap, anyway, and then to his shoulders and finally onto the crown of his head. Nobody offered to lend him the fan so he took it without permission and sat on the lookout.

On this day, too, demons came gathering there and began to gamble. The old man hurriedly made a noise by hitting the fan and imitated a rooster's crow.

"Is it dawn already?" exclaimed the demons. "It's awful soon!" They jumped up in confusion, but one of the young demons could not get away because his long nose got caught in the hook over the hearth.

"Help! Wait for me, demons. My nose is caught on the hook," he cried.

Unconsciously the old man let out a chuckle.

"Listen! There's the voice of a man," the demon said.

They all looked around here and there until they found him. Down they dragged the old man from the top of Jizō's head and all pitched into him. Instead of gathering up the money which the demons left, he barely got away with his life.

That is why people say that one should not imitate others so much.

(Mogami-gun, Yamagata)

69. THE WIND GOD AND THE CHILDREN

A strange looking man suddenly came up to where children were playing on the grounds of a shrine one autumn day.

"Even if you can play here, you don't have anything to eat around, do you?" he said. "Wouldn't you like to go where there are lots of chestnuts and persimmons and pears? I could let you eat enough to fill a big kettle. How about it?"

"Do you mean it?" the children asked. "We would like to go to a place like that, but aren't you lying?"

"I really mean it, I'll take you, all right," he answered. He stuck out something like a long tail behind him and said, "Now everybody straddle this and hold on tight. Are you all on?"

"Yes, we're all on!" they cried.

Then he blew a puff of wind and began circling up into the sky. Presently he set them down where there were lots of chestnuts and persimmons and pears. Then he blew another puff and knocked down a lot of fruit and nuts for them. The children ate all they could and then played around.

After a while it was evening. The man said, "Here, while you have not been noticing it's already evening. I have to go somewhere else now, so you go on home by yourselves, see?" With that he rode off somewhere on the wind.

This surprised the children. They thought they couldn't go home any more and began to cry. In the meantime it grew pitch dark. Then they saw a light far away. They went towards it to see.

A big fat woman came out. She asked, "Where did you come from?"

The children answered, "We were given a ride on something long by a man from somewhere and came here on the wind. He gave us lots of chestnuts and persimmons and pears, but he went away then and we can't go home."

"Is that it? That fellow is my good for nothing boy, South Wind. You certainly were thoughtless children!" declared the old woman. "I'm the mother of the Wind Gods. I'll send you home right away on my boy called North Wind. You don't need to worry."

She brought the children into her house and gave them a fine supper of white rice and bean soup. Then she called, "Boy, wake up!" She woke up North Wind who was asleep.

The children got onto North Wind's tail. He made a puff like his brother had done and took them back to their village. The whole village was in an uproar hunting the children because they had not come home at night. When they came back blown by the North Wind, everybody in the village was happy.

> — Kenichi Mizusawa,
> *Tonto Mukashi Attagedo, Dai Isshū*, p. 162
> (Yamakoshi-mura, Koshi-gun, Niigata)

70. THE TWO TUMORS

Long, long ago there was a priest who had a big tumor over his eye.* While he was traveling around various regions practicing austerities, he came to a certain village in the mountains where nobody would let him spend the night. All he could do was to go into an old wayside shrine to spend the night.

Toward midnight he heard the footsteps of a crowd of people who came into the shrine. Looking closely, he could see that they were *tengu*, long-nosed demons, who had gathered there for a drinking bout. He could not hope to stay hidden all

---

* Another well-known version in story books pictures the tumor on his cheek.

night long. He watched his chance, and in spite of being scared, he hung his straw cushion over his seat and jumped out. He joined in their dance.

Toward dawn the demons began to get ready to go home. They said, "Come again next time because you are a jolly priest. So you will not just agree to come and then break your promise, we will take this to keep as a pledge." As they said that, they took the tumor from over his eye and carried it away with them.

Glad to get rid of the annoying tumor, the priest returned to his own region in great delight.

It happened that in his neighborhood there was another priest bothered with a tumor in exactly the same place. Hearing the talk of what had happened, he was so envious he couldn't stand it. He inquired in detail about the man's story and then set out to the shrine just to get his tumor taken off.

In the middle of the night, just as he had expected, the long-nosed demons gathered for their drinking bout. Hurriedly he tied the straw seat to his hips and did a dance for the demons.

"Great! You kept your word without a hitch, old fellow, and you came back, didn't you?" they shouted. "To pay you back for your trouble, we will give you back your pledge."

He felt something slapped onto his face. All at once he found that he had a tumor over each eye. He was sorry for ever after because he overdid imitating somebody.

— *Seisuisho*

71. THE OLD MAN WHO SCATTERED ASHES

Long ago out in the region of Ōshū, too, a good old man and a bad old man lived as neighbors. They both went on the same night to catch little fish in the river and left something called a *do* fastened there.

The old man from the upper house got up early the next morning to see, but in his *do* there was only a little dog. In the *do* belonging to the man in the lower house there were lots of little fish. He took all the fish from that *do*, threw the puppy from his into it, and went home looking as though he knew nothing.

The old man from the lower house went afterwards to see and found a cute little puppy crying in his *do*. He lifted it out and carried it home to raise it carefully. It grew bigger day by day. When the old man fed it from a bowl, it grew as big as the bowl; when he fed it from a pot, it grew as big as a pot. In a short time it was big enough to carry all kinds of tools on its back and go with the old man into the mountains.

One day the dog showed the old man how to catch deer in the mountains. The old man called, "*Shishi* that way, come here! *Shishi* this way, come here!"

The deer came gathering from all directions, and the dog caught them one after another and killed them. Then the old man put them on its back to take home. He and his old woman cooked deer soup.

While they were eating, the old woman from the upper house came along. After she heard all about what had happened, she said, "Please lend us your dog, then. We want to eat deer soup, too." She led the dog away.

On the next day the old man from the upper house took the dog to the mountains. The dog didn't say to load him with things, but the old man wanted to take this and thought he might as well take that as he put a hatchet, a sickle, and all kinds of tools on its back. Then with a shout, "Hurry, there, hurry!" he drove the dog into the mountains.

Instead of saying *shishi*, the old man made a mistake and

called, "*Hachi** that way, come here! *Hachi* this way, come here!"

All the bees in the mountains came flying and stung the old man. He was furious and declared it was all the dog's fault. He struck the dog and killed it. After burying it under a rice-tree, he went back home.

No matter how long the old man at the lower house waited, his neighbor did not bring his dog home. When he went to ask for it, he found the old man there groaning in bed.

"Thanks to that dog, the bees stung me all over like this," he complained. "He was such a hateful beast I killed him and buried him under the rice-tree. If you want your dog, you can go and look for him under the rice-tree."

The old man from the lower house felt very sad when he heard this. He went to the mountains and cut down the rice-tree. From its wood he made a hand-mill. He and his old woman sang a song as they turned it:

> "Money, come down before *jiji;*
> Rice, come down before *baba.*"

As they sang the hand-mill song, money came down in front of the old man and rice came down in front of the old woman. In a short time they became very rich. They could afford to eat rice every day and wear fine clothes.

The old woman from the upper house came along again and asked, "Where did you get all those good things?"

"Where do you think?" they answered. "We cut down the rice-tree in the mountains where your old man killed our dog and buried him, and from the wood we made a hand-mill. When we grind it, money and rice come out. That's where we get them."

"Then lend me the mill," the greedy old woman demanded and borrowed it to take home.

Now the old man and old woman at the upper house ground the mill with all their might, but they forgot the very important words to the song. They sang:

> "*Baba* come down before Grandpa;
> *Shishi* come down before Grandma."

---

* In Tohoku dialect the words for deer and bee both have a sound like *shigari*. The bad old man in the tale confuses the important words in italics in this and following passages.

Lots of bad smelling things, according to the words, came flowing into the house. The old man and old woman were furious and blamed it all on the hand-mill. They split it up with an ax and poked it into the fire, burning it all up.

The old man and old woman at the lower house waited quite a while and then went to get the hand-mill.

"That hand-mill was an outrageous thing," the neighbors complained. "It filled our house with filthy things. We could not stand to have it around, so we split it up and burned it in the earthen stove."

"If that's what happened, I can't do anything," said the old man. "Give me some of the ashes, at least, for me to take home."

He brought a basket and carried the ashes home in it. When he took the basket of ashes out into his garden to scatter them, he discovered that geese had alighted on the pond next to it. The old man began to throw the ashes and sing the following words:

"Ashes, go into the eyes of the *gan*;
Ashes, go into the eyes of the *gan*."

The ashes flew into the eyes of the geese as he sang and they dropped dead. The old man gathered them up and went home. He and his wife made goose soup. While they were enjoying it, once more the old woman from the upper house came.

"How do you get such good things to eat?" she asked.

"You folks chopped up the hand-mill from our house and burned it, so I brought back the ashes and tried scattering them. A lot of geese fell down," answered the old man.

"If that's it, let me have a little of those ashes for us," demanded the old neighbor.

Again she made her old man imitate the neighbors. He climbed onto the ridge of his roof one night when a strong wind was blowing. Looking up at the sky, he began to scatter ashes, but again he forgot the important words. He bellowed away:

"Ashes, go into the eyes of *jiji*;
Ashes, go into the eyes of *jiji*."

As he sang, the ashes flew into his eyes, according to his song, and blinded him. He went tumbling off the roof.

124

The old woman waiting on the ground was watching for geese to fall and took him for a goose. The story goes that she hit him with a big mallet.

— Kizen Sasaki, *Esashi-gun Mukashibanashi*, p. 15
(Esashi-gun, Iwate)

72. THE OLD MAN WHO SWALLOWED A BIRD

Once upon a time an old man was working alone in his garden patch in the hills. When it came noon, he ate his lunch of thick gruel paste he had brought. What was left over he pasted onto a branch of a tree and lay down beneath it for his nap.

A titmouse flew there and its feet got stuck in the thick gruel. The sound of it fluttering as it struggled woke the old man up. He felt sorry for the little bird as he watched it and decided to lick the sticky paste off its feet. While he was doing it, the little bird slipped into his mouth along with the paste and he swallowed it.

The startled old man patted his stomach where the little bird was jerking around. There was something by his navel. When the flustered old man pulled at it, he broke wind with the sound of *chichin pyo pyo goyo no ontakara*.

He told his old woman about it when he got home. He tried pulling the feathers sticking out of his navel, and it made him break wind just as before. The old woman thought this was so amusing that she urged him to go and let the feudal lord hear it.

The next morning he set out to the castle. He began to cut wood behind it.

"Who's that cutting my lord's bamboo?" challenged a guard as he came up.

The old man thought, "Here's my chance!" Aloud he said, "This is the greatest at breaking wind in all Japan."

"Well, then, if you're the greatest at breaking wind in all Japan, let's try having you do it for my lord."

The retainer led the old man into the castle and into the presence of the feudal lord. The old man pulled the titmouse's feathers sticking out on his stomach and broke wind *chichin pyo pyo goyo no ontakara*.

The feudal lord and everybody who had lined up to watch enjoyed it immensely. Great honors were bestowed upon the old man, and he went home with many gifts.

— Takeshi Makiuchi, *Shinano Mukashibanashi Shū*, p. 161
(Nagano)

73. THE SOUND OF CHEWING ACORNS

Once upon a time an honest old man went out into the mountains to gather firewood. He started back down when it was getting late. He happened to notice some acorns at his feet, so picked up three.

Before he could reach his home, the sun set and all around became dark. There was nothing to do but spend the night at a dilapidated shrine at the foot of the mountain. There he went to sleep.

In the middle of the night he was awakened by a big noise. When he looked around, he saw a throng of demons beating the floor boards with iron rods and shouting, "Come forth, gold! Come forth, silver!"

The old fellow huddled up and shook with fright. Suddenly he remembered the acorns he had picked up on the path. He took one out and crunched it between his teeth.

The demons were startled at the noise. They looked at each other and asked, "What's that? What's that noise just now?"

The old man took out another and crunched it between his teeth.

The demons were even more frightened. "This is terrible! It sounds like the place is going to pieces!" they shouted. "Let's get away! Let's run!"

Without looking back they all rushed off. The next morning the old man saw gold and silver scattered over the floor. He raked it all up and took it home in high glee.

In the neighborhood a bad old man lived. He was envious when he heard what had happened. He set out immediately for the mountains to imitate him and bring home treasure.

At night when the crowd of demons came along, he crushed an acorn with his teeth.

"That's the sound we heard last night, but the place didn't go to pieces, did it?" exclaimed the demons. "And all the treasures we got out with so much trouble are gone. This certainly is somebody's trick."

They ransacked the place and finally found the old neighbor. "This is the fellow who played the trick on us last night!" they roared and beat him up soundly.

— Tōzō Suzuki, *Kawagoe Chihō Mukashibanashi Shū*, p. 90
(Kawagoe, Saitama)

74. THE JIZŌ MADE OF WHITE RICE CAKE

Once upon a time there was a childless old couple who made a living from their many patches of wheat and millet.

One year a big crowd of monkeys came to their fields and began eating the crop before the wheat and millet was completely harvested. No matter how often the old man chased them off, they would return and ruin the plants.

He decided upon a scheme. He got his old woman to make a lot of soft white rice cake. Then he took off his clothes and plastered it all over his body. He went out to his garden and struck a pose like a Jizō image to guard things.

The monkeys gathered there again, but they couldn't enjoy eating the grain with Jizō staring at them. They decided to carry him across the river. All together they lifted him and carried him over singing:

"What if monkeys get washed away,
Don't let Jizō get washed away.
Yoo-ra-san, yoo-ra-san!"

Once they were on the other bank of the stream and set the old man down, his body seemed to lean a little.

The chief monkey noticed this and shouted, "Jizō is tipping over! Bring the thousand *ryō* box and prop him up."

The other monkeys brought the money box from somewhere. The old man managed to keep from laughing while they propped him up on one side. Then without a word he changed his position and tipped toward the other side. The monkeys brought out one more box and placed it on that side. After that they all went back across the river.

The old man took the two boxes of money home. He and his old woman rejoiced together over them.

There was an old couple living next door. The old woman came to borrow some live coals and heard how this old man got the boxes of money. She became very envious.

She went home and promptly made a lot of soft white rice cake. She had her old man undress even if he didn't want to and after plastering it all over him, she made him go out to their patch of garden.

The monkeys came out as they had done before, picked up the old man, and started across the river with him while they sang the same song. This old man could not keep from bursting out with a laugh.

The monkeys were furious when they heard that. They cried, "You make-believe Jizō! You fooled us yesterday, too, and carried off our two boxes of a thousand *ryō*!"

They clawed the old man until he was covered with blood.

— *Tabi to Densetsu,* Vol. XVI, No. 5, p. 20
(Kakunodate-machi, Senhoku-gun, Akita)

The Wolf's Eyebrows

75.   THE WOLF'S EYEBROWS

Once upon a time there was a very poor man. He had no more food or anything. At this rate he could not go on living, so he thought he might as well get a wolf to kill him.

He went off to the mountains. That night a wolf appeared, but he did not try to eat the man although he saw him. That was not the way it should be.

"Why don't you eat me?" asked the man.

The wolf answered, "Just because we see a human being, we don't eat him. We only eat those who look like men but really are animals. There is no reason to eat a real man like you."

This seemed strange to the man. "When people all look the same, how do you know who are real and who are not?" he asked.

"If you look with this hair from my eyebrow, you can see," said the wolf as he pulled one out and gave it to the man.

The fellow accepted it. If he couldn't get the wolf to eat him, he could at least try becoming a pilgrim. He set out on a pilgrimage to Shikoku.

At one place he stopped at a lonely house to ask if he could spend the night. The old man was generous and was going to let him stay, but the old woman came out scowling and refused.

The man remembered then about the hair from the wolf's eyebrow. Thinking this was just the time to try it out, he took it from the folds of his robe and held it up to his eye. The old woman looked like a cow.

Yes, it was as the wolf had said. He loaned the hair to the old man to see. It was just the same for him. Instead of seeing his old woman, he was looking at a cow.

— Tsuneichi Miyamoto, *Yoshino Saiō Minzoku Saihōki*, p. 294
(Daitō-mura, Yoshino-gun, Nara)

76. HOW A FOX RETURNED A KINDNESS

Very long ago an old man found a bean in the corner of his yard one morning while he was sweeping it. Thinking it was too good to leave there, he planted it in the garden behind his house. Soon it sprouted and grew into a big tree. It did not yield as much as the Hachikoku tree, but this one bean tree had nearly a bushel of them on it.

A fox came along one day, however, and ate up every single bean. The old man turned red with rage.

"You hateful beast," he roared, "you have stolen and eaten all the beans I have taken such pains to raise! I'll beat the life out of you!"

"I'm terribly sorry. Please forgive me," begged the fox. "If you let me go, I'll help you earn lots of money."

"All right then," said the old man, "I'll let you off."

The fox turned himself into a pony at once. The old man led him to a rich man's house and sold it for a big price, making lots of money. The fox ran away in four or five days and came back.

"This time I will change myself into a teakettle," he said and turned into a kettle of just the right size.

The old man took this kettle to the temple and sold it to the priest who liked tea. The teakettle made a nice sound when the priest put it over the fire.

The novice took the teakettle to the river to scour it.

"Ouch! Ouch!" it cried. "Don't rub so hard."

"This is awful," reported the boy. "The teakettle said something."

"Nonsense," replied the priest. "How can that be?"

He built a big fire and hung the teakettle over it.

Finally the fox could not stand it any longer and cried, "That's too hot, Priest! *Gage-e!*" He showed his tail and ran off.

— Kunihiko Uchida, *Tsugaru Kōhi Shū,* p. 27
(Goshogawara-machi, Kitatsugaru-gun, Aomori)

77. CHŌJA FROM A WOODEN IMAGE

A poor man was doing labor for a *chōja*. At that house there was a splendid gold image of Buddha. The worker was always wishing that for once in his life he could worship such an image as his very own. Since he was only a laborer, it seemed out of the question for him to realize such a wish.

One day when that worker was cutting wood in the hills, he happened to find a piece of wood that looked exactly like an image of Buddha. He picked it up and carried it home. Three times a day he brought his bowl of rice to offer it and worshipped it in his own room.

This went on for several years. His master and the servants looked on from a distance and laughed secretly about him. The fellow was honest and worked very well, however, and his master was uneasy for fear the fellow might go somewhere else to work. He was always trying to think of a way to keep him working there for a long time. Finally he decided upon a plan.

The *chōja* called this worker to him and made the following proposal. "Let's have a wrestling match between the wooden image of Buddha which you worship these days and my gold image of Buddha. How about this for an agreement? If your wooden image loses, you agree to work for me for the rest of your life. If my gold image loses, I will give you everything I own."

He called a great number of his men servants and maids together as witnesses and bound the bargain firmly.

The poor worker turned pale when he heard this. He went to his room and knelt before his wooden image in the alcove. "My own Buddha, something terrible has happened! My master has pressed an unjust demand upon me which I can never meet. I am going to carry you on my back and run away now, so please understand," he entreated.

The wooden image said, "Don't rush around! Don't rush around! There is no reason to get excited. I'll try a match with the gold image. Don't worry."

The master sent for the worker to come and bring his

image in a hurry, so he reluctantly carried it into the big hall. Then the master brought his image out. A crowd of servants came as witnesses. The master set the images in their places and announced to the two of them they were going to be made to wrestle because of this and that reason. Then he raised his fan suddenly as the signal.

Strangely enough, the two images began to wobble forward and draw near to each other. For two hours they pushed each other around. At first the servants only looked on thinking it was strange, but presently they began to encourage the wooden image. They called, "Don't give in! Don't give in!"

The master got red in the face urging his image, "Don't give in! Don't give in!"

In the meantime perspiration began to flow all over the body of the gold image. The way it moved gradually grew sluggish. The *chōja,* too, intent only on it began to sweat big drops. His face was crimson as he begged, "Gold image, don't give up! Haven't I always worshipped you as the greatest treasure in this house? What do you mean by losing to a mere wooden image? Brace up, brace up!"

But the gold image only seemed to grow weaker. Suddenly it let out a scream and fell over without enough strength to get up again. The wooden image pushed it out and sat upon what had been worshipped until then.

Thinking there were strange things going on in the world, the people, one after another, who had been looking on, worshipped the wooden image on an altar.

The defeated *chōja* picked up his gold image dejectedly and left the house according to the agreement as the worker who owned the wooden image became master in his stead.

The *chōja,* who had left his house carrying his gold image, traveled here and there on foot, gradually becoming impoverished until he became destitute. One evening he found himself on a broad meadow at sunset. He reflected upon the change which had come to him. He faced his image and complained, "Gold Buddha, Gold Buddha, why did you lose to that sort of wooden image? It isn't enough that you are too weak to do anything, but I have to be reduced to these hard straits."

"Master, it's too late now," replied the image. "It's true that the other one was just made of wood, but every day it received three offerings of rice and it was worshipped devoutly. You offered me a bowl of rice only two or three times a year at a festival or anniversary of a death. How do you expect me to have strength to put into things? Besides, the real reason I lost my strength is that you don't have true faith."

They sighed together. It was really true and the master could not say a word in reply. He went around carrying the gold image of Buddha and being a poor man for the rest of his life.

— Kizen Sasaki, *Rōō Yatan*, p. 23
(Tōno-machi, Kamihei-gun, Iwate)

78. THE LISTENING HOOD

This story is also about a good old man who was poor and lived out in the country of Ōshū. He had always wished that he could offer fresh fish to Inari Sama, the tutelary deity, but he was too poor and couldn't do what he wanted to.

One day when he went to the shrine to worship, he said, "Ujigami Sama, Ujigami Sama, I want to say that because I am so poor, I cannot offer you fresh fish. So please eat me instead, I beg of you."

"Old man, old man, there is no reason for you to worry so," replied Ujigami Sama. "I know very well what trouble you have, and I am going to grant you a bit of fortune. Here, take this precious hood I give you and try putting it on your head. When you wear this, you can understand everything that birds or beasts say." With these words he bestowed upon the old man a faded red hood.

"I thank you very much indeed," said the old man. Quite pleased, he hurriedly tucked the old red hood into his bosom and left.

As he went wandering down the road, he noticed a big tree

by the side of the road. Stopping there to rest, he soon fell asleep. Now from the direction of the beach a crow came flying and lighted on a branch of the tree because it was tired. Presently another crow came flying, this time from inland, and stopped in the top of the tree. The old man saw them and decided that if he were going to try the Listening Hood which Inari Sama had given him, now was the time. He pulled it out quietly and put it on. Suddenly he heard the voices speaking overhead.

The crow that flew from the beach said, "Well, it's been a long time since I saw you. I have been at the seashore up till now, but there aren't any fish there these days. The times are hard, so I flew this way. Which way did you come from?"

"I came from Arima way. It looks like hard times anywhere you are," answered the second crow. "Is there anything unusual going on in the world?"

The crow from the seashore answered, "It isn't very unusual, but it has been five years since the rich man in a village by the beach built his storehouse. When they were laying the thatch over the entrance to it, a snake somehow or other crawled up and happened to be nailed below a board. It cannot get away and it's still there, half alive and half dead. What I can't help admiring is the way the female snake brings food and keeps it alive, but they both really are having a hard time.

"Their resentment has built up until it has come to afflict the body of the rich man's daughter with a lingering illness," continued the crow. "If the board isn't taken off soon, the snake will die and so will the daughter. Time after time I fly there to the roof to call the people, but human beings are a sorry lot and can't understand what I am saying."

"Men are just like that," the second crow agreed. "They seem absolutely numb to such things. Well! I'll see you again one of these times," he added as the two crows separated, one flying to the east and the other to the west.

The old man thought he had heard something good! He wanted to hurry to the rich man to save his daughter and the snake, too, but he could not set out because he was not ready. He went loitering along behind the town until he found a round wooden box which was broken and thrown away. He picked it up and pasted paper on it. Then he set it on his head and went before the gate of the rich man by the beach, calling "Fortune Teller! Fortune Teller!"

The rich man at that time was worried about what to do for his daughter who had been sick for so long. He called from inside, "Hey, out there! Fortune Teller, come in quickly and lay out your divining sticks."

The old man went in and asked, "What kind of a fortune do you want me to read?"

"My daughter has been sick for a long time," explained the rich man. "In fact, it is at a point now where we don't know but what she may die today or tomorrow. Try a fortune to see if there is something which we can do to make her recover."

"Then lead me where the sick girl is," the old man demanded.

He went in beside the pillow of the sick girl and sat down. Then he began chanting over and over, "Arrowroot leaves which spread twenty *ri* have spread twenty *ri*." After this he told them in detail the story, just as he had heard it from the crows.

The rich man declared that it was all exactly as the fortune teller had said. Such a thing might have happened, so he called a carpenter to tear off the boards in the roof to see. There the snake was, nailed down and half of it turned white with decay.

"Oh, this is it," they said.

Carefully laying the snake in a basket, they lifted it down from the roof. They put it in front of the drain and fed it. After they had cared for the snake for some time until it was strong, they turned it loose. While this was being done, the daughter's illness began to disappear day by day like the peeling off of layers of thin paper. As the days went by she completely recovered.

The delighted rich man gave three hundred *ryō* to the old man in thanks. He became rich then. He went back home and immediately built a new shrine for Ujigami Sama and celebrated with a more splendid festival than had ever been held before. Needless to say, he also offered fresh fish many times.

The old man of the Listening Hood put on good clothes

this time and set out again on a trip. When he was resting under some big trees one day, crows came flying from the east and the west again and rested in the branches of that tree and began gossiping.

One of them said, "I get tired of staying in one town all the time."

The other answered, "That's right. The following sort of thing is going on in the town where I have been until now. The rich man at the town has been sick for a long time. It looks like his life will be over any day now. The reason is that when he built an annex five or six years ago, he cut down an old camphor tree which had been in the yard a long time. The stump is under the eaves where the rain drips off onto it. Since the root cannot die as long as it has life, it continues to send out shoots, doing its best to grow because of its vitality. But as fast as it sends out shoots, they are pruned off. Thus it cannot die even if it wants to, nor can it live any better if it wants to. Its resentment has gradually afflicted the master and he lies sick.

"And besides, it is touching to see the friends, the trees from various mountains, that come almost every night to try to cheer up the suffering stump," added the crow. "I would say, if they mean to let it live, they should let it live. If they mean to kill it eventually, they should dig it up, roots and all. It's a great pity."

As soon as he heard the story, the old man hurried to town.

"Fortune Teller, Fortune Teller, we have something to ask you," called the people of the rich man's house and invited him in. "Our master is sick. Find out for us what we should do to make him well."

The old man said, "There should be an annex here which was built five or six years ago. Let me spend the night there."

"Why, Fortune Teller," exclaimed the people at the house, "how could you know that we have an annex?"

"That I learned through my fortune telling," he answered. "At any rate, leave me there for the night. In the morning I will tell you all about the cause of the master's illness. Do not let anybody come in until I say so."

That night he stayed there alone to see how things were.

In the middle of the night he heard a rustling and footsteps drawing near. A voice said, "Dear Camphor Tree, how do you feel?"

A faint answer seemed to come up from deep in the ground. "Are you the willow tree from Rokkoshi-zan who is saying such kind words?" it asked. "I'm sorry you always have to come so far and with such dicuffilty. I am just as you see, wishing I could die even one moment sooner. But it can not happen that way, and I can only go on suffering."

"Now don't give up that way," the friend said, trying to comfort him. Then he went away.

After a while something came along with a swishing sound. A voice asked, "Camphor Tree, old friend, how goes it?"

Again the camphor tree's voice came up, "Is it the creeping vine from Hayachine-zan who is asking? There is absolutely no way to save me. I am sorry for the way you fellows have to come to comfort me every night."

"Oh, it's nothing," answered the voice. "You mustn't worry about it. I'm on my way to Goyo-zan for a good time, and this is on the way. It isn't like the east trying to meet the north. You will be well by spring. Just wait and see. Don't be discouraged."

Then the creeping vine went on his way with the same swish.

With the Listening Hood on the old man heard all that was said. When morning came he asked to be led to the pillow of the sick man. There he did his usual chant about the arrowroot spreading twenty *ri*. Then he told in detail the conversation of the trees he had heard the night before.

"This isn't just the suffering of the camphor tree under the eaves," he concluded. "All the trees even on the high mountains in every direction are miserable over this. Hurry and dig up this root."

They dug up the root and worshipped it as the Tree God of their yard. The master's illness then began to disappear day by day, like the peeling off of layers of thin paper. All the rich man's house rejoiced and again the old man received three hundred *ryō* in thanks.

The old man accepted the money and went home, but from that time he had no more desire for gain. He stopped telling fortunes and spent his days living like an ordinary rich man.

— Kizen Sasaki, *Rōō Yatan*, p. 86
(Tsuchibuchi-mura, Kamihei-gun, Iwate)

79. THE DEIFIED GILTHEADS

Long, long ago in Tosa province a fish vendor was going from the beach to a village back in the mountains to sell fish.

He found a copper pheasant caught in a net set by somebody among the trees along a lonely road. When he saw the bird, he wanted it, but he knew that it would not be right to take it without paying. Since there happened to be nobody around, he took three giltheads from his basket and put them in the net, taking the bird without permission and carrying it home.

Villagers came along soon after this and thought it very strange that giltheads were in the mountain. They thought it even more strange that they were in a copper pheasant's snare. In the belief that it was a sign from heaven, they deliberated together and hurriedly built a little shrine. There they joined in worshipping the three giltheads, calling the shrine Kurodai Shansho Gongen, the temporary manifestation of heaven in the three giltheads.

As the fame of the shrine began to spread, people came from all directions to worship, and it became very prosperous. By the time the fish monger came along again and told how he had taken the copper pheasant, the shrine had already become very popular.

(Kōchi)

138

80.   THE MOUNTAIN GOD AND THE BOY

Long ago a mother lived with her only son. By going to the mountains every day to gather firewood she barely made a living.

When the boy was eleven or twelve years old, he faced his mother and said, "I have been a burden to you all this time. Now I am going to go to work instead of you. Please stay at home from today."

The boy started going to the mountains every day. His mother gladly made a lunch for him every morning.

One day after he tied his lunch to a branch and climbed the tree to cut dead branches, a white-haired old man came along. He untied the lunch from the branch and started eating it, all the time looking up at the boy.

The boy climbed down with his load of dry wood and said, "Old man, the lunch Mother made was good, wasn't it?"

"Thanks. When we get old we are hungry," answered the man.

The boy told his mother what had happened as soon as he got home. She said, "You did right. I'll tell you what. Tomorrow I'll make two lunches. You can eat one of them."

The next morning she sent him off with two lunches. The boy took them and while he was working as usual, the same old man came along and ate a lunch. The boy climbed down and said, "Mother made me two lunches today, old man. If one is not enough, please eat the other, too."

The old man ate them both up.

On the third day the boy brought only one lunch. He said to the old man, "Mother is going away today so I must go home early. I brought only your share."

The old man appeared and called to the boy who was starting to climb the tree. "Wait a minute," he said. "There's something I want to tell you. As a matter of fact, I am a *Kami Sama*. Listen carefully to what I am going to tell you. Please start on a pilgrimage now to the great temple at Tenjiku. Along the way you will probably be asked to do some favors so you should agree to do them." He had scarcely finished speaking when he suddenly turned into an oak.

The boy told his mother about this and she gladly agreed to let him go. Although they had decided he should set out for Tenjiku, there was not enough food in the house for him to eat on the way. They decided he should go to the *chōja* living in the neighborhood to borrow some rice and bean paste.

"What do you want it for?" asked the *chōja*.

"I happen to be going on a pilgrimage to the temple at Tenjiku," replied the boy.

"That's lucky for me," exclaimed the *chōja*. "I want to ask a favor of you. My daughter has been ill for three years now and she never seems to get better. She is still very weak. Please pray there that my daughter can be cured."

The boy said, "Certainly, I will."

He borrowed the rice and bean paste and set out for Tenjiku. Twilight came on as he was walking and he asked to spend the night at a great mansion.

The master of the house asked, "Where are you going?"

They boy explained and concluded, "And that's the reason I am on my way to Tenjiku."

The master said, "That is fine for me. You see, I make a living here selling *sandan* flowers, but recently the original tree and the second have both withered. It makes it difficult for me with only the third tree. Since you are going to Tenjiku, please pray at the temple that the first and second trees can bloom again."

The boy agreed to this, too.

The next morning he asked to have a lunch packed and was about to set out. The master said, "Further on you will have to cross a big river."

Sure enough, after the boy had walked a while he came to the big river and there was no bridge across it. "Now what shall I do?" he exclaimed. As he stood there bewildered, he saw a hideous woman walking along the opposite bank. Her face was so swollen he could hardly tell where her eyes and nose were. "Hey, you, over there," he shouted. "How can I cross this river?"

Strange to say, the woman promptly crossed the river to where the boy was. "Just where are you going?" she demanded. After she had heard his explanation, she said, "I have lived on land for a thousand years, in the sea for a thousand years, and in the river a thousand years. I am not a mortal. I want to go back up to Heaven but I don't know how. Here I am with my eyes and nose all swollen, wandering around on the face of the earth. When you get to Tenjiku, won't you please ask the *Kami Sama* there how I can go back up to Heaven?"

The boy agreed.

"All right, then" she said and putting him onto her head, she landed him on the bank across the river in a twinkling.

Far in the distance the boy saw a magnificent temple. He took courage joyfully and went toward it. There he found the old man he had met in the mountain before.

"How many days did it take you to get here?" the old man asked.

"I came with only one night's rest," he answered.

"Did anyone along the way ask you to attend to something?" the old man asked.

The boy began with the story about the daughter of the *chōja* in his neighborhood.

"Oh, that sort of thing," commented the old man. "The *chōja* must call together all the men working for him and every male in the neighborhood. He must tell her to serve them wine. If he gives all his property to the one she pours wine for, she will recover immediately."

The boy told about the *sandan* flowers next.

"Ancestors of that family buried a golden jar at the foot of each of those trees. The descendents always seem to remain ignorant of that. The flowers have withered so they can find out. When the jars are dug out, if you get one and leave the other for the family, the original tree and the second will come back to life immediately. Was there anything else you were asked to do?"

The boy told about the ugly woman.

The old man said, "If you meet her, tell her this—'If you just give one of those *ninjo* jewels which you are keeping so greedily to a mortal, you can ascend any time.' Is that all, then, all that you were asked to do?"

The boy replied, "Yes, that's all."

Once more the old man turned into an oak.

The boy then set out on his return trip and arrived at the bank of the river. The former ugly woman was waiting for him and asked what he had found out.

"Take me across the river first. Then I'll tell you," he said.

She put him on her head as before and in a twinkling she had glided across.

The boy said, "You have two jewels, haven't you? Don't keep them covetously forever. Give me one and then you can climb back up."

"All right, then," she said and handed him a jewel.

At the same time there was a frightful noise in the distance and all around was instantly covered with a thick mist. The frightened boy started running as fast as he could. When he managed to get some distance away, he looked back. The mist had cleared and a waterspout reached high into the sky. The woman was riding up on it. He put the jewel he had received into the fold of his kimono and walked on.

Soon he reached the house where the *sandan* flowers were kept. When he repeated for the master what he had heard at Tenjiku, the man promptly dug by the roots of the trees. As a result, the golden jars were discovered. When he gave the boy one, the withered original tree and the second one sent out green shoots. The boy took the jar and went joyfully on his way.

Now the *chōja's* house was left. When he repeated for him what he had heard from the old man at Tenjiku, the *chōja* promptly called together all the men who worked for him and every single male in the neighborhood. At the house he tried asking his daughter to pour wine for each one. The girl refused to pour wine for anyone there. Only the boy across the street who had just returned from Tenjiku remained.

The *chōja* said, "You're a male, too. Please see if my daughter will pour you a cup of wine."

The girl immediately picked up a cup and offered it to him, but the boy refused to accept it.

"This is the desire of *Kami Sama*. Please accept it," the *chōja* urged.

The boy then received the cup of wine. The girl recovered instantly and getting to her feet, she performed a dance.

The boy with his mother moved to the *chōja's* house and he married the girl. They lived happy forever after.

— Ichirō Iwakura, *Okinoerabu Mukashibanashi,* p. 239
(Okierabujima, Ōshima-gun, Kagoshima)

81. THE SUCCESS IN LIFE OF THE THREE BROTHERS

Once upon a time there was a couple with three sons. One day they went together to dig in a garden patch. When the father went later, it was already noon, but he saw them working hard without lifting their heads.

Then they stopped for a rest. After they had finished their lunch, one of the boys when to the privy and began shooting blue flies with a tiny bow for fun. Then the three of them did nothing but shoot flies. One would say, "Good, I hit its wings!" Another, "Well, I hit its head." And so they played until sunset. Then they went home.

The father who had been watching them was angry. "I won't let such lazy fellows as you stay at home," he said. "Leave at once!"

There was nothing else to do so the three of them set out. As they walked along they came to a place where the road parted into three directions. They talked it over and decided the oldest should take the upper road, the second the middle one, and the youngest the lower road. Before they parted from each other, they agreed on the day, month, and year when they would meet there again.

The oldest boy walked along the upper road to where a crew of carpenters was building a house. He stood and watched them silently.

One of the carpenters came over to him and said, "Would you like to become a carpenter's apprentice?"

The boy thereupon took up carpentry.

The next brother went along his road to where a lot of men were practicing archery. He joined them and became an apprentice to a master archer.

The youngest came to a place where men were practicing thieving. He stayed with them and learned to become a thief.

Thus each of the three began working hard in his chosen way. After a while the day drew near upon which they had agreed. Each asked to be permitted to leave his work and started for the former road. The oldest was the first there, the next brother followed, and the youngest was the last to arrive.

He asked, "Master Eldest Brother, what work have you been doing?"

The brother replied, "Mine has been carpentry."

He then asked, "Master Second Brother, what have you been doing?"

That brother replied, "I learned archery."

"Then both of you eat well," remarked the youngest.

"How about Master Third Brother?" asked the other two.

He only mumbled something and would not give a clear answer.

"You must have been following the thieving trade," they said. "At that you can't eat."

He only asked, "Are each of you carrying a purse?"

In about as much time as it took each to say, "Yes, I am," he had relieved them both of their purses. He laid them aside and said, "Then take them out and see."

No matter how they searched there was a good reason they could not find them. Then he brought out the two purses and showed them. They said, " You should manage to eat if you are that alert."

They went on home together.

It happened that about that time the only daughter of the feudal lord had been kidnapped by a demon and he could not succeed in rescuing her. An official notice was proclaimed that a reward of anything desired would be given the one who brought her back.

The three brothers saw this and declared, "This is the right kind of work for us. If the three of us join together, we will certainly show him we can bring her back."

They set out for the demon's stronghold. When they reached there, the demon was making the girl pick lice off his head while he was taking an afternoon nap.

"Carpenter, make a doll," ordered the youngest brother. That brother hurriedly made a doll, the very image of the girl. The youngest brother slipped it into the place of the girl and they climbed into a boat and fled from the shore.

When the demon awoke and looked around, he found a wooden doll by his side. He was so furious he chewed it into bits.

He looked out and saw the sails of the boat fluttering as it sped away. He hurled his harpoon and caught a hold on it. Then he started pulling it back. It was drawn nearer and nearer to land.

As it came almost within reach of the demon's hand, the youngest brother called, "Shoot, Master Second Brother!"

Putting all his strength into the shot, the second brother sent an arrow into the neck of the demon, killing it.

The three brothers returned the girl safely to the feudal lord and received a great reward. They lived a happy life after that.

— Ichirō Iwakura, *Koshikijima Mukashibanashi Shū*, p. 38
(Koshikijima, Satsuma-gun, Kagoshima)

82. THE STAR CARRYING A LANCE

Once upon a time there was a *chōja* who had seven sons. In his neighborhood lived a poor family with an only son. These children all studied at the school run in the temple.

One day their teacher gave them a special task. He said, "Bring boats and we will race them on the river."

Since the *chōja's* children were rich, they hired a carpenter to make their boats, but the poor boy could not do the same. As he was crying alone about this, a man who practiced ascetics came by and asked him what was the matter.

The ascetic said, "If that's the trouble, bring me some scraps of wood and some clay."

With the wood the boy brought he made a little boat and from the clay he made a little doll to stand at the helm. The boy thought to himself that with such things he could never win over the *chōja's* boys. He felt very unhappy.

When he took his boat to school the next day, the *chōja's* boys laughed and made fun of it. The time came to take their boats to the river to see how they floated. Strange to say, the little figure on the boat the ascetic made took hold of the helm from

146

the right and started moving. The boy thought the boat made of scraps of wood and clay would surely sink, but it sailed faster than those of the *chōja's* boys. He was delighted.

Outdone this way by the poor boy, the others were bitterly resentful. They wanted to find a way to get even with him.

One day their teacher said, "I want each of you to bring a fan on which a bird is drawn."

The *chōja's* sons immediately went to a fan shop and bought fine fans. They hired an artist to draw a rooster on each. The poor boy went home at a loss about what to do. While he was pondering over it, the ascetic he had seen before came by. He mended a torn fan the boy had and painted a rooster on it for him.

When the boy took his fan to school the next day, it crowed. The teacher was astonished. "If it crows again, it is certainly a treasure bird," he said.

He had barely said so when it crowed, *"Ke-ke-ko-ko."*

That meant that the *chōja's* boys had lost again. They were furious that the poor boy had beaten them for the second time. They picked up lances and chased him. Their teacher stepped between to stop them. In a moment they were all changed into stars.

On Sanagijima they say now that the *shichisei* stars (Pleiades) are the *chōja's* sons. The *neno* star is the poor boy and the one standing among them is *yarae* star, the teacher of the temple school. They have said since that time that the one farthest in front is holding a lance.

— Akira Takeda, *Sanuki Sanagi-Shishijima Mukashibanashi Shū,* p. 39
(Sanuki Sanagi-Shishijima, Nakatado-gun, Kagawa)

83. WHY THE SEA IS SALTY

Very, very long ago there were two brothers living in a certain place. The older brother was rich, but the younger brother was poor.

Although the next day would be New Year's Day, the younger brother could not prepare for it. He went to his brother to borrow a measure of rice, but he only cursed him and refused to give him anything.

There was nothing for the younger brother to do but go home. On the way he met an old man with a long white beard cutting grass by the side of the road.

"Where are you going?" asked the old man.

"Tonight the Old Year ends, but I have no rice to offer the God of the Old Year, so I am just walking around with nothing to do," he answered.

"That certainly is too bad. I will give this to you," said the old man as he took out a little wheat *manjū* and handed it to him. "Take this and go to the little shrine in the woods over there. Behind the shrine there is a hole where many Little People go in and out. I am sure they will want your *manjū*. Tell them that you will only trade it for a stone hand-mill and then all will be well."

When the man came to the shrine in the woods he had been told about, sure enough, there was a hole where lots of Little People were running in and out in great confusion. Wondering what they were doing, he saw they were falling over each other, struggling to carry a single piece of thatching rush.

"Here, I will carry it for you," offered the man. He picked it up in his fingers and carried it for them.

While he was doing it, he suddenly heard a tiny voice by the mouth of the cave cry, "Murder! Murder!"

Looking around carefully, he found that one of the Little People had got caught between the cleats of his wooden *geta*. He picked him out gently.

"What a big, strong man he is," they all exclaimed, and

looking up, they discovered the wheat *manjū* in his hand. They brought out a lot of gold and piled it up in front of him, but because he had been warned by the old white-haired man, he said he would only trade it for a stone hand-mill. He finally got the mill.

"Even among us Little People there is not another treasure like this," they said, "but we will give it to you for the *manjū*. Turn the mill to the right, and anything you want will come out. Turn it to the left and it will stop," they explained.

He took it home carefully. His wife was all worn out from waiting for him.

"It's the close of the Old Year and where have you been?" she scolded in a high voice. "Did you bring the rice?"

"Well, just wait and see," he replied. "Hurry up and spread out a piece of straw matting."

Setting the little hand-mill down on the mat his wife had spread out, he began turning the little mill saying, "Come forth, rice! Come forth, rice!"

Over a peck of rice came pouring out. Next, he ordered salmon to come out. Then one after another he ground out all kinds of things he needed. That night he and his wife observed the happiest sort of Old Year's passing and then lay down to sleep.

The next morning was New Year's. The man said, "Here I am, suddenly rich. I don't want to go on this way, just living in somebody's lean-to. First, we'll build us a new house."

They ground out a beautiful house and then a storehouse twenty by thirty feet came out next. They got a long house for workers and a stable with seven horses to go with it. At last they ordered, "Come forth, rice-cake! Come forth, wine!"

They prepared a big celebration for all the neighbors and relatives. The village folk came in great astonishment to enjoy a feast such as they had never seen before. Even the elder brother, who had refused to lend the measure of rice, was invited.

"How can he have become so rich in just one night?" the brother wondered. He thought it so strange, so very strange, that he could not get over it. Surprised as he was, he noticed this and that very carefully.

Then finally it came time for the guests to go home. "I would like to give the guests cakes to take home," thought the younger brother, secretly going into a corner to start turning the hand-mill. He said, "Come forth, cakes. Come forth, cakes."

"Ah, now I understand," said the brother, who had been spying. "It's the hand-mill."

After all the guests had gone home that night, the older brother chose the time when the younger brother and his wife were sleeping to steal back into the room where the little hand-mill was hidden. He carried it away and with it he took *mochi* and other cakes that were beside it. He carried them all down to the beach where, as luck would have it, there was a little boat. He loaded the precious mill and all into it, untied the rope, and rowed out to the open sea, planning to cross to some island to be a rich man by himself.

Although he was loaded with *mochi* and other cakes and such sweet things in the boat, he unfortunately had nothing salty. He thought that he wanted to get salt out before anything else and recklessly began turning the mill.

"Come forth, salt. Come forth, salt," he said and salt began pouring out.

Soon the boat was full of salt. But when he thought that there was about enough salt and wanted to stop it, he did not know about turning it to the left to stop it. The salt kept on running out until at last, from the weight of the salt, the boat, the elder brother, the stolen hand-mill, and everything went sinking into the sea.

Because nobody knows about turning the mill to the left, that hand-mill is still grinding out salt at the bottom of the sea. That is why the water of the sea is salty.

— Kizen Sasaki, *Rōō Yatan*, p. 293
.(Kamihei-gun, Iwate)

84. THE RICE-CAKE TREE

Two brothers lived in a certain place. The older one was rich and the younger was poor, but the older one was good-natured while the younger was quite shrewd. The younger one wanted to fool his brother in some way so he could make some money off him.

Finally he thought of a plan. He went to the hills and brought back a tree that had a nice appearance. He then made rice-cake and stuck pieces of it onto the tree. He carried it to his brother's house and announced cleverly, "Elder Brother, wouldn't you like to buy a tree that grows rice-cake? It's a special kind of tree, for if you pick the rice-cake and eat it, plenty will grow again!"

The older brother looked at the tree with the rice-cakes on it and believed what his brother said. He paid a lot of money and bought it. But when he had eaten the rice-cake on the tree, there was only an ordinary tree left. There really was no reason for rice-cake to grow on it again. Realizing he had been fooled, he lost his temper and went to his brother's house to scold him.

"Wait a minute," protested the younger brother. "Which rice-cake on the tree did you start with when you ate it?"

"From the biggest piece," answered the older brother.

"That's the reason why no more grew," explained the younger man gravely. "The biggest piece was the parent, the one that grew the crop."

— Tōzō Suzuki, *Kuttan Jijii no Hanashi*, p. 167
(Nii-mura, now Toyotama-mura, Shimoagata-gun, Nagasaki)

85. CLEVER YASOHACHI

Long, long ago there were six men with the name Yasohachi living in a village in Ōshū. Without nicknames, nobody could tell which was which. One was gruff and quarrelsome, so he was called Gedō or Yasohachi the Cur. The one who liked to gamble was called Bakuchi or Gaming Yasohachi. The one who planted rice fields was called Hyakushō or Farmer Yasohachi. Another sold rice and was called Komeya or Rice Dealer Yasohachi. Another, a thief, was called Nusuto or Sneak Thief Yasohachi. The last was clever so he was called Funbetsu or Clever Yasohachi.

One day Yasohachi the Cur had a fight with Gaming Yasohachi and giving him a heavy blow, he killed the man. The Cur had not intended to kill anyone and this frightened him. Worried about it, he went to Clever Yasohachi to talk over what he should do.

Clever Yasohachi advised, "Try taking the corpse to the water inlet of Farmer Yasohachi's rich field. Set it carefully in a squatting position on the little path between the paddies where the inlet is cut and leave it there."

Now Farmer Yasohachi came around that night checking on the water in his rice fields and found a stranger sitting by the water inlet to his paddies. "You sneak! How dare you come around stealing water again?" he shouted and gave him a thump from behind with a stick.

The body toppled over. When Farmer Yasohachi looked closely, he recognized Gaming Yasohachi. "Now what have I done? What am I going to do?" the frightened farmer thought. Taking a gift with him, he went to Clever Yasohachi for advice, also, just as the Cur had done.

Clever Yasohachi said, "I advise you to tie the body up in an empty straw rice bag and carry it to Rice Dealer Yasohachi's store. Put it up on the very top of the stack of rice bags in front and leave it there."

Then the next night Sneak Yasohachi came by Rice Dealer Yasohachi's rice store. Thinking the sack was full of rice, he stole it. When he got it home and opened it, there was Gaming Yasohachi's dead body. He was aghast and wondered what to do. Finally he, too, went to Clever Yasohachi with a gift to ask him to lend him his wits.

Clever Yasohachi said, "Well, after it gets late tonight, go to Gaming Yasohachi's house with the body and knock on the door from the outside and say, 'I'm home now.' His wife will be sure to get angry and say something cross and refuse to open the door. Then take Gaming Yasohachi to the well by the gate and throw him in."

Sneak Yasohachi did as he was told. He tapped on the door of Gaming Yasohachi's house after midnight and disguised his voice. "I'm home now, old girl. Open the door," he demanded.

From the inside the old wife let out an angry shriek, "What do you mean by getting back so late? A good for nothing like you would be better off dead!"

Then Sneak Yasohachi took the corpse to the well and after he dropped it in with a splash, he stole quietly away.

The wife raised a great clamor when she heard that sound. She called the men from the village to help pull him out. When she saw him, she wept and cried bitterly.

Only Clever Yasohachi made something out of the affair, receiving gifts from all of them.

— Kizen Sasaki, *Rōō Yatan*, p. 233
(Tsuchibuchi-mura, now Tōno City, Kamihei-gun, Iwate)

86. THE TWO BOLTS OF WHITE CLOTH

Long, long ago a bride and her mother-in-law got into an argument when they took the May Festival doll out of its box to get ready for the Boy's Festival.

"This doll is called Tawara Tōta," one said.

"No, it's Hachiman Tarō," the other said.

Neither would give in to the other. Then they agreed to take it to the priest the next day and let him decide which was right.

That night the mother-in-law quietly took a bolt of white cloth to the temple and asked the priest to let her win. A little after she returned, the bride took a bolt of white cloth, also, and asked the same thing of the priest.

On the next day the two went together and said, "One of us is wrong. Dear Oshō San would surely know which is, wouldn't he?"

The priest laughed and answered, "This is neither Tawara Tōta nor Hachiman Tarō. From here is a bolt of white and from there a bolt of white for nothing — in other words, it is called Nitan-no-shiro Tadatori."*

(Minamiazumi-gun, Nagano)

---

* A play on words: *nitan no shiro tadatori*, two bolts of white cloth for nothing and Nitan-no-shirō Tadatori, a popular hero of legends.

154

87.   NIŌ AND GAŌ, THE TWO DEVA GODS

Long, long ago Gaō came from China to match strength with Niō of Japan.   Niō said that he wanted some dumplings made for the feast.   His wife tore an iron pole into bits, sprinkled bean meal on them for tea cakes and served them.   This was to test Gaō Sama, but he went through it doggedly, eating every one and saying that they were very good.

Niō declared, therefore, that they should be brothers and guard the gate of Kannon Sama together forever after.   And that is why, even now, one of the Deva Gods stands holding an iron rod.   The other one, the one with his mouth open, is said to be Gaō from China.

(Minamiazumi-gun, Nagano)

88.   A SILENCE MATCH

Long, long ago a man and his wife who lived in a certain place liked rice-cake more than anybody else did.   They made some once and ate so much that only a little was left.

"Tonight let's see who can keep still the longest.   The one who wins can have what is left of the rice-cake," they agreed.

Unfortunately, a robber came in and went walking around in the house looking for things.   The couple were quite aware of it, but whoever said anything would lose the rice-cake, so they both kept stubbornly silent.

The thief took advantage of this, looking all over, scattering things around.   Finally he opened the cupboard and started to take out the rice-cake box.

The wife could not stand it any longer when she saw this. She cried out, "Oh, that thief is carrying off the rice-cake."

Her husband had held in until then, but he roared, "That rice-cake is mine, now."

How about it?   Do you think the robber agreed?

89. RAT SUTRA

Long, long ago a man took his dog with him and went hunting in the mountains. Night came on and he asked to stay at a lonely house.

An old man and an old woman lived there. One of them turned to him and asked, "Is there a good sutra said in your village?"

"Yes, there is," he said.

"Then won't you please teach it to us?" they said.

The hunter was embarrassed because he could not recall the words of the sutra. He gazed up at the ceiling wondering what he should say. Just then a rat came hesitantly out onto the rafter.

The hunter intoned, "*Chorochoro suruno wa nanjyai na* (what's that coming out here)?"

The rat crouched low.

He continued, "*Sora soke shyagoda* (look it crouches)!"*

The old couple listened thankfully for having been taught such a fine sutra. Every day after that they repeated the chant over and over together:

"*Chorochoro suruno wa nanjyai na*
Sora soke shyagoda."

One night a thief broke in and was moving around stealthily looking things over. Just at the same time the old couple were chanting their sutra before their family altar.

"*Chorochoro suruno wa nanjyai na*," they intoned.

The thief thought he had been seen and crouched in the shadow of the door.

"*Sora soke shyagoda!*" they continued.

Absolutely certain that they were talking about him, he ran off in a flurry. The old couple, quite unaware of what had gone on, continued their prayer.

— *Mukashibanashi Kenkyū*, Vol. I, No. 7, p. 46
(Minamata-machi, Ashikata-gun, Kumamoto)

---

* When given the proper intonation, these words sound surprisingly like a sutra.

90. THE FROG WHO IMITATED MEN

This is a story told in a mountain village called Nisattai in Ninohe-gun, Iwate.

Long, long ago in a place like the river in Nisattai, there lived a frog. One day a horse dealer came riding along from Kunohe way, contentedly singing, headed toward Fukuoka.

Looking out at him, the frog thought he would like to give forth with the same kind of voice. He tried it with a "*Gee-gee!*" No matter how he did it, he could not sing with a good voice.

While the frog was working away at it with all his heart, the horse dealer came to a halt, astonished at what he heard. He looked all around but couldn't find anything. There was only a frog saying, "*Gee-gee.*"

"What are you doing?" he asked the frog.

"You have such a nice voice, I am imitating you," it said. "Where are you going?"

"I'm setting out on a pilgrimage to Ise," answered the man. "If you want to go along, I'll take you."

That pleased the frog. He leaped up onto the horse's back and rode along with the man. They crossed a mountain, passed through a village, and finally drew near Fukuoka.

The frog was thinking things over on the horse's back. "Wait a minute," he thought. "When men stand on two feet and walk, there should be no reason why I can't stand up and walk, too. Good, I'll try it!"

He jumped down from the horse and started walking on his hind legs. After he had walked for a while, he saw a place that looked like Nisattai.

"Well, this is strange," he thought. "Are there other places that look the same as Nisattai!" He came to a stop and rested for a while. Then he looked around again. He found that he was back where he lived.

A frog's eyes are behind it, so when it stood on two legs,

it was looking behind and he walked backwards. That is why he went back to his starting place.

When we imitate folks, we are just as foolish.

— Isamu Kikuchi, *Ninohe Mukashibanashi,* p. 82
(Nisattai, Nisattai-mura, now Fukuoka-machi, Nihohe-gun, Iwate)

91. THE BLACK LINE ON THE BROAD BEAN

Once upon a time there was an old woman living alone. She decided to do some cooking. When she took out some beans to put into the kettle, one bean happened to fall and roll toward the corner of the yard. When she brought some straw out to start her fire, a breeze came up and blew one piece of it into the corner of the yard. After she had the fire burning and was working, a burning piece of charcoal fell out and it, too, rolled toward the corner of the yard.

The bean, the piece of straw, and the live coal, which had met in this way in the corner of the yard, talked it over and decided to set out then on a pilgrimage to Ise. When they came to a stream, the piece of straw acted as a bridge for them.

The bean and the red charcoal argued about who should cross first.

"I'll go first," said the charcoal.

"No, let me," said the bean. Finally it was settled that the charcoal would cross first.

When the charcoal got half way across, it got scared and began to tremble. It couldn't go on. In the meantime the straw caught on fire and the two of them fell into the stream together.

The bean looking on called, "That's your punishment!" It laughed so hard it burst open, *pachin.* It began to cry over that. A seamstress came along there and asked why it was crying. It told what had happened and showed her its belly.

"Oh, that's too bad!" said the seamstress. She took out a needle and thread and sewed it up. Unfortunately she had no

green thread. All she had was black. That is why even now
the broad bean has a black line on its edge.

— *Shizuoka-ken Densetsu Mukashibanashi Shū,* p. 596
(Yoshikawa-machi, now Hamamatsu-shi,
Hamana-gun, Shizuoka)

92. THE CENTIPEDE'S ERRAND

Once a centipede, a flea, and a louse gathered together on a
cold day.

"Why don't the three of us drink some wine together on a
day like this?" the centipede suggested.

They all agreed, but then they had to decide which one would
go to buy it.

The flea said, "I always jump along, *pinpin,* and the jug
might get broken. I can't go on such an errand."

The louse said, "I walk *guzu-guzu,* terribly slow, so I am
afraid I cannot be of any help."

There was nothing for the centipede to do but go himself.

No matter how long the flea and louse waited, the centipede
did not come back. They got impatient and decided to see what
he was up to. They found him busy doing something in the
corner of the yard.

"Hey, Mister Centipede, what are you doing," they called.
"It's getting late."

Without turning around, he replied, "I have a lot of feet
and I am still fastening sandals onto them."

— Kenji Matsuo, *Iōjima-mura Kyōdo Shi,* p. 120
(Iōjima-mura, Nishisonoki-gun, Nagasaki)

93. SEIZŌ'S RABBIT

Long, long ago Seizō went to the mountains to play with his friends. There in the grass a rabbit lay fast asleep.

"Oh, here's a dead rabbit in a place like this!" exclaimed one of his companions.

Seizō immediately held his nose and said, "No wonder. I thought something smelled terrible."

Just then the rabbit, hearing voices of people, woke up and ran off frightened.

"Oh, he was just taking a nap," remarked another of the friends in surprise.

Seizō quickly interposed, "That's why—I thought his ears seemed to be moving."

94. THE PIGEONS MIGHT OVERHEAR

Long ago an old man in a mountain village was working in a garden patch on the far side of the river.

An old man on the other side called, "Hey, what are you planting today?"

The man who was planting didn't answer. He only beckoned for the other to come over.

The other man crossed the stream and went up to him asking, "What's the matter?"

The old man put his mouth to his ear and said, "I'm going to plant red beans."

"What's so secrect about red beans?" the other asked.

"Well, it wouldn't do if the pigeons overheard," he answered.

— *Azuma-gun Shi*, p. 1404
(Azuma-gun, Gumma)

95. THE INSECT THAT TAPS ALONG WITH A STICK

Long ago a blind minstrel, carrying his lute on his back, was passing through a mountain village.

An old man called from the garden patch on one side of the river to an old man on the other side, "Hey, look over there. A big insect has come out tapping along with a stick. Six years ago when a bug like that came out, we had a big harvest of beans. We should have a big crop again this year, too."

96. THE QUILT ON THE NAPE OF THE NECK

Long ago a poor man who slept in straw instead of under a quilt said to his children, "You must not tell about sleeping in straw because I am ashamed of it. You must say *quilt* before people." He trained his children carefully.

When he and one child went calling once, the child said, "Father, there is a blade of quilt stuck to the back of your neck."

97. THE *KINOMATA* LETTER AND THE BLACK LETTER

Once upon a time an old woman and her daughter lived in a little village in the mountains. It was decided that the girl would go as a bride to a place which could only be reached by crossing the mountain and over a valley.

"If you have a chance to come for a visit, don't come alone because it is too far and dangerous," cautioned her old mother. "Be sure to have somebody make the trip with you."

The girl set out but she did not come for a visit and there was no word from her. The mother was very worried.

One day a neighbor came and said, "I've an errand to attend to in the next village. Do you have a message to send to your daughter?"

His kindness delighted the old woman. She said she would like to have him take her girl a letter. She went into the back room and seemed to be writing something. She came out again and said, "Well, then, please give this to my girl." She handed a letter to the neighbor.

The man thought, "What a smart old woman she is! I didn't know she could write a letter." He was surprised and could not get over admiring her.

He went to the next village and handed the girl the letter. She read it with delight and wrote an answer. She said to him, "Please deliver this to my mother."

This filled the man with even greater admiration. "This is really wonderful. The old lady is smart and her girl is, too," he thought as he went home and delivered the answer to the mother.

To tell the truth, neither the mother nor the daughter knew a single word. In the old woman's letter was a row of signs like a tree fork which could be read *mata* (then). She meant by them, "Then daughter, then why, then you, then don't come?"

Her girl understood what the signs were. For her answer she painted over the entire page with a solid coat of charcoal ink. She meant by that, "I want to visit you but I haven't a bit of time to go."

Her mother understood that immediately.

— Kenichi Mizusawa, *Tonto Mukashi ga*
Atta Gedo, Dai Isshū, p. 62
(Yamakoshi-mura, Koshi-gun, Niigata)

98. PRETENDING TO KNOW

Long ago when a certain man was invited to eat out and had noodles for the first time, he asked the serving child, in a low voice, "What name?"

Thinking the man was asking his name, the boy replied, "Yajirō."

The man remembered that. The next time he went to town with some villagers from his place, he saw a lot of noodles hanging out to dry.

"Look! Look! See how much *yajirō* is out drying," he said. "I wish I could order some of that cooked and give you all a treat."

99. CHILLED PRIDE

Long, long ago a proud samurai spent the night at a farm house in the country.

The farmer said, "It is very cold tonight. Please cover yourself with this straw matting."

"I have gone to battle time after time, and when I slept in the open, I never needed anything over me," boasted the samurai and lay down to sleep on the bare floor.

In the night it became very cold and he was uncomfortable. He wakened the farmer and asked, "Say, Farmer, do you make the rats in this house wash their feet?"

"No, we don't do anything like that," was the answer.

"Don't you? Then the rats will soil my clothes when they run over them," he said. "Bring me a straw mat and I will put it on to protect myself."

100. THE HOARDER

Long, long ago in a certain place there was a very grasping old woman. Whatever she saw anybody have she wanted.

She would say, "If you don't want this, would you let me have it?" Then she would carry it off.

One time a neighbor's cat caught a rat and ate it all except the tail. The people were about to throw that away and jokingly said, "Surely the old woman would not ask for this."

Gossip about somebody and she appears, so the old woman came to call just then. When she saw the rat's tail, she said, "If you don't need this, would you let me have it?"

Everyone was puzzled. One asked, "What are you going to do with it?"

"I want to make a sheath for my drill," she replied.

Chilled Pride

101. STINGINESS

Long, long ago two stingy old men lived as neighbors. One of them sent a messenger to his neighbor.

He said, "I want to borrow a hammer. Tell him that I beg him to lend me a hammer for just a little while."

The neighbor asked the messenger, "Now is that nail an iron one or wooden?"

The messenger replied, "He is going to pound an iron nail."

The neighbor cocked his head on one side and said, "It is such a trifling request, but I happen to have loaned my hammer elsewhere and I do not have it now." With that he sent the messenger home.

When the master heard what the reply was, he said in disgust, "What stingy people there are in this world. He wanted to know whether it was a wooden nail or an iron nail, did he? He lied and refused because he was afraid I would damage his hammer. He just made an excuse. Can you beat that? Well," he concluded, "I'll have to get my own hammer out, I guess."

102. TEMPTATION TO STEAL

Long, long ago a man went to call on somebody on a day when snow had fallen. The outside was so bright that when he went into the house it seemed pitch dark.

"Oh, how dark, how dark," he exclaimed as he went in.

At the entrance he stepped on something cold. Picking it up, he discovered it was a little hatchet. He thought that a little hatchet like that was just what he had been wanting and he was tempted. He tucked it carefully into his bosom, supposing that nobody could see.

After a little while he realized that the inside of the house was dimly light and that the people there had been able to see what he had done. He had got himself into a fix and he began squirming around, wondering what to do. He kept talking and waiting for a chance. Then somebody else came visiting.

The new visitor, also, exclaimed, "Oh, how dark, how dark!"

At that the man who had stolen the hatchet said, "Here, I have a good cure for that. I'll show it to you. If you put a little hatchet like this in your clothes for a while, it will be light for you soon. I just came in and tried it out, so I am sure it works."

He took the hatchet from his clothes and handed it to the caller.

103. THE SON-IN-LAW'S CHAT*

Long ago before a son-in-law first went to his father-in-law's home, he had been told by some of his friends that he should prepare some smart small talk to bring out at the right time. If he just ate and kept mum, they said folks would laugh at him.

When the day came and the first greetings were over, trays of food were brought in and the feast started.

The son-in-law stood his chopsticks up on his lap awkwardly and began his little chat. "I say, Mr. Father-in-law, how about it? Have you ever seen a snipe as big as a man can put his arms around?"

"Why, I have never seen anything like that," was the answer.

"Oh, haven't you?" remarked the son-in-law. "I never have seen one either. That is all."

---

* The stupid son-in-law is a favorite subject for jokes. The humor of this tale lies in its lack of a point.—Tr's. note.

104. THE ROOF OF THE UNDERGROUND WORLD

Among stories about big liars there are many unusual ones.

Long ago they dug a well in a certain village. No matter how much they dug, they still could not reach water. Day after day they kept digging until at last they came to some smoked straw.

They were about to tear that out to start digging further when a voice thundered, "What are you fellows from the upper world trying to do? That's the straw from my roof. What do you mean by peeling it off?"

105. THE GAMBLER'S TRIP TO THE SKY

Long, long ago a gambler who was going home after losing heavily sat himself down under a big tree and began rolling dice by himself. He seemed to be having a good time, shouting, "Won! Lost!"

A long nosed demon was looking on, wanting the dice very much. The man traded them for the demon's feather fan.

The demon said, "If you fan a nose with this fan, it will become longer—a little longer with light fanning and much longer with strong fanning. Turn the fan around to fan and the nose will grow shorter."

The man took the fan and stood by the gate of a rich man's house. The only daughter of the family was just leaving to visit a shrine. The man looked at her nose and began fanning with all his might. Her nose grew seven feet long and she had to give up going. All she could do was to lay her nose on its side in the big parlor and cry every day.

The rich man put up a big sign that said he would let anyone who could bring his daughter's nose back to its former size become his son-in-law. The gambler tucked the fan into his bosom and presented himself to try for the award. Little by little he made the girl's nose shorter and everybody in the house was delighted. Quite elated, the man lay down to cool himself and went off to sleep, continuing to fan himself in his sleep. His own nose faced the back of the fan, so it began to grow longer and longer. It finally grew so long that it reached Heaven without his knowing it.

Now it happened at that time they were repairing the Milky Way in Heaven and they needed one more pillar for the construction. While they were looking around for one, a pole rose up suddenly from below. Thinking that this was a piece of luck, they brought a rope and tied it securely, tilting the tip a little.

The pain woke up the rich man's son-in-law and he discovered what had happened. In great excitement he turned his fan around, fanning his nose frantically, but it was too late. Instead of his nose shrinking down to the man, his body was drawn up.

The gambler floated clear to Heaven toward the end of his nose because it was fastened down as the support for the bridge.

Therefore there should be a dice shooter from the earth even now in the bottom of the Milky Way, but one cannot see him with an ordinary telescope.

106.   A TRIP THROUGH THE SKY

Long, long ago there was a man who had good luck in anything he did. He shot geese with a gun bent like the character *he* (ㅅ). With a single shot he brought down tens of geese flying in a line one after another.

He tied them all up and hung them from his waist. Then he started walking along the road. The geese came back to life and flew off somewhere in the sky. They set the man down on the top of a five-storied pagoda at a certain temple in Yamato.

The man wondered how he could ever get down from there and called loudly for help. Many people from the temple and the village gathered below him. They took the biggest *furoshiki* there was at the temple and held it out firmly by the four corners at the foot of the pagoda. Then cotton was heaped as high as a mountain on top of that. The man was told to jump carefully onto it.

With a one, two, three, he jumped. Under the force of his landing, the *furoshiki* instantly closed up and the four priests who had been holding the corners bumped their heads together so hard that fire flashed from their eyes. The fire caught in the cotton, and then the *furoshiki,* the pagoda, and the man who had been dropped by the geese onto it all burned up.

Only the tale is left from long, long ago.

APPENDIX

INTRODUCTION

To the Japanese Edition

It has not been an easy task to undertake to plan revising the volume *Nippon no Mukashibanashi* (Japanese Folk Tales),* which has been read with pleasure by young people of Japan for a long time and even now has lost none of its attraction, but I have had the project in mind for some time, wanting to carry it out although quite aware of the difficulties involved. While I kept saying presently, presently I would get to it, this problem alone seemed always to be set aside in the midst of my various painful attempts to cope with the sudden changes which occurred in the world since old age overtook me. Even a greater problem than this in my purpose has been that some who had been interested were carrying out plans independently and were not inclined to go through this laborious task once more, and it was difficult to find help from new directions. As a matter of fact, it might have ended merely as a cherished desire of my many former associates and mine, a kind of prediction that if happily it might be carried out, this and that meritorious deed would be rendered.

Fortunately for *Nippon no Mukashibanashi,* Miss Hisako Maruyama and Miss Yasuyo Ishiwara, two ladies who had experienced the disasters of the times, had really been interested in this problem all along. Sometimes because of my old age I was ready to give up hope of concluding the work on the folk tales. There were times when I would spitefully consider leaving the task to the ladies, then again I would reconsider; and there

---

* *Nippon no Mukashibanashi Shū, Jō.* Tokyo Ars, 1930; with a revised title, *Nippon no Mukashibanashi,* Shunyōdo Shōnen Shōjo Bunko, 1934; Mikuni Shobō, 1942; Jiipusha, 1951; and Kodokawa, 1953. The latest edition had thirteen printings between 1953 and 1958. The texts of these five editions are identical. The revised selections have had seven printings to date.—Tr's. note.

were days when I would hesitate and complain that if these tales which existed even before recorded literature, these orally transmitted tales valued throughout long ages and bearing traces of their routes and changes as they spread over the face of the world, were left by me to the natural changes under present conditions, they would be broken up and scattered around. Perhaps only these two ladies really understood my almost pathetic dilemma and courageously decided to take on the difficult work with me. To be sure, this revision is not the final word. If it were possible, I would like to train more comrades and progress to where they would form a research center for folk tales from everywhere.

A long introduction for a tiny book is a joke, but since there are many people I hope will take this occasion to read what I set down, I will add a few further remarks. It has been nearly thirty years since *Nippon no Mukashibanashi* made its appearance in the world. My studies have advanced somewhat since then and at the same time the collection of Japanese folk tales has increased greatly. Formerly those collected could be said to have been mainly from the northern end of the main island, but at present they are from nearly half of the prefectures, cities, and *gun*, stretching southward to the Amami Archipelago as far as the farthest Ryūkyū Islands. To be sure, among these tales there are some with greater detail and others that are briefer, some which truly represent the original story while parts of others have been forgotten or supplemented. With what we have, however, we can see they do not belong to just one region, to be found in only one place. Occasionally we may find an unusual example that has been preserved, but while we are regarding it with caution, we have the pleasure of unexpectedly finding one of the same type in a ditsant region, making it easy to separate imitation folk tales or those that have been fabricated.

We have no proof as to when the Japanese term *hanashi* (tale) of *mukashibanashi* originated, but it is not found in literature before Middle Antiquity.* Even now in the Tohoku area,

---

* See Sen-ichi Hisamatsu, *The Vocabulary of Japan Literary Aesthetics.* Tokyo, 1963, p. 2-3. Hisamatsu uses the single term Antiquity for the period from the Third to the Twelfth centuries (Yamato and Heian Eras).—Tr's. note.

northeastern Japan, the term *kataru* is used to express it. Judging from examples from *Konjaku Monogatari** it is possible to conclude that ordinary conversation was also referred to as *monogatari*. After that term came to be applied to more pretentious speech, the use of a word like *hanashi* arose. Any explanation that *hanashi* was used because the tales were *hashinashigoto* (without a beginning or ending—unimportant) or the like is hardly acceptable. Even now in western Chūbu the word *hanashi* is usually not used as a verb.

When we consider the matter, we realize that the term *mukashibanashi* always seems to have had a special meaning attached to it when it was used. In old sacred songs of the Ryūkyū Islands the parallel phrases, *mukashi kara, kesashi kara,* frequently appear. It is clear that it is not the present, but the time is not settled. We cannot be sure how far or near it is to our present, but from the beginning it was a past which was not reckoned. Procedures in literature may be different nowadays, but it appears to me that people in the past occupied a world which they did not wish to confine within settled terms, one where they wanted to enjoy dreams.

Even if terms used in Occidental countries are translated as *minwa* or *minkan setsuwa,* those who encounter them do not feel inclined to adopt them. Such terms do not carry across to old people who have heard many kinds of *mukashibanashi* and remember them, hoping to tell them to their grandchildren or other young people. Those who ask, "What is a *minwa?*" really know the old forms of Japanese tales and want to transmit them without falsifying them and to leave them as they are for the next generations. We might say as much about the term *minyo* (folk song), but clever young people learn these as they do literature and do not hesitate to transmit them with changes.

By now there are only a few remaining who recollect our precious oral tales, their number having dropped sharply during the confusion of war years. Surely it is better to continue our endeavors to prevent the loss of these tales which barely remain in

---

* Latter Heian Era, probably around 1050. See Kokusai Bunka Shinkokai, Ed., *Introduction to Classic Japanese Literature.* Tokyo, 1948, p. 97 ff.—Tr.'s note.

nooks of various villages. There may be many who have already given up, saying it is too late by now for such search, but in spite of that we are trying in our small way.

I have had some dissatisfaction about this one volume, *Nippon no Mukashibanashi,* which was completed thirty years ago at a time when collection of tales had just begun. I think it is reasonable even now to think there are people who will slap their thighs and smile understandingly, even in regions which seem to yield no more tales, for young people who left their homes at an early age but now return only to find that the old people who liked tales have gone and there is no longer anyone to ask about them, or in places where everybody in town seems to be busy working in factories and do not appear to understand the feelings of anyone who wants to engage them in talk or there often seems to be nobody willing to be helpful.

I recall printing over a thousand copies of a book I called *Mukashibanashi no Saishū Techō* (A Memorandum for Collecting Folk Tales) in 1936 and distributing them to elementary schools in as widely scattered regions as possible. In it I gave a rough outline of one hundred well-known folk tales, leaving blank pages for each for entries, and at the beginning of the book I wrote as briefly as possible some directions which I thought would be helpful to collectors. I sent a letter with each booklet, stating that if the recipient would share the results of his search with me, I would in turn make a gift of the volume to him. Not a single book with a "Yes, I have completed it" came back, but many letters of thanks or acknowledgement arrived, and later I frequently heard from people who saw it.

Tochigi Prefecture and others were areas which had interesting folk tales, but perhaps recipients were waiting until they could complete the work exactly or were too busy, for not a single person returned the *Techō.* I no longer recall the name of the school principal of the village, but he reported to me that he took the *Techō* home and read it to his mother, wife, and children around the open hearth. After he had finished, a hush fell over them and then the women sighed deeply. He said that one of them asked, "Are there really people even in Tokyo who like to hear such tales?"

At the time I showed the letter to some young people and suggested that after a while they go and follow it up, but I think the matter was dropped with that.

As I look back now, I realize this was a hasty way of going about it. For instance, if I had not asked for all of the tales to be hunted, probably at least a third of them would have come back with, "There! It's done!" I think it was too business-like a method, too American.

There were some at the time who were critical and said, "What do you expect? Do you think anyone nowadays will go along with such a plan?" But "nowadays" then seemed a bit different. A few years before that I had put out two special numbers devoted to folk tales in the well-read magazine, *Tabi to Densetsu* (Travels and Legends), asking for contributions of folk tales from the local regions of readers all over the country. Among the subscribers were some of my acquaintances and the number of manuscripts that were contributed were enough to fill the greater part of the number with many insuitable ones still left over. For the Volume IV Number 4 (1931), the first special number, I wrote an article entitled *Mukashibanashi Saishū no Shiori* (A Guide to Collecting Folk Tales), which now is published as a separate book. At the time there were no particular results worth mentioning, but I think it heightened the ardor of local scholars.

For the issue three years later, the December number of 1934, there were newcomers represented among the contributors who sent in things that were not collected tales but freshly written items, *minwa,* giving the impression of stories to promote Communism. I had already heard rumors about them and was considering the possibility that something of the line might be coming in, so it was a good lesson for me. I suppose people are free to make such practical use of literary mediums, but our point of view to the last is historical and we were cautious because we did not want to offer false material to those who wanted to know folk tales. And then until very recently some seem to be offering things hardly fit to be called literature, things invented to suit some motive, which they circulate under the name *minwa*. Leaving aside the "isms" or "policy" involved, to call such things *minwa* is contrary to literary tradition. Just as a precaution against infringing upon such territory, we ourselves avoid calling folk tales *minwa*. We do not want to confuse villagers of Japan by having them use such a word.

My remarks have dragged out longer than I had expected, but there are a couple of circumstances that I should include in closing. One is about the little magazine called *Mukashibanashi no Kenkyū* (The Study of Folk Tales)* which I planned. It was taken over and put out for a full year beginning in 1935 by *Tabi to Densetsu.* Then during a little more than one year it was left to a certain publisher, but the place lacked vigor and within the second year that publication was terminated. Our work seemed lighter for a while, but presently we braced up, for we had not reaped many advantages from the venture.

But *Tabi to Densetsu,* under the management of Masanori Hagiwara, continued. He had a sincere love for the islands of his old home in Amami and had made many friends within and outside them. He put out the magazine from early 1928 till nearly the close of 1943 without a break, cultivating hitherto unknown territory in our studies. The academician, Seijo Nakamura, for one, and other scholars whom we had overlooked freely sent in accounts of their travels and impressions as articles. Although it may have appeared pressure tactics, when I had surplus copy, I would offer it to his magazine and as these articles accumulated, I put them out in book form.

Of even more value were students returning to their own homes in the Amami Archipelago and even students from Okinawa, who told about their home islands. Among such were Ichirō Iwakura of Kikaijima and others who made their appearance and were determined to contribute all kinds of material which could never be duplicated. Although my study of the folk tale can be considered only partial, my habit of always combining my country from south to north as a whole in my thinking and enjoying the various ideas that came to light were due largely to hints I received from *Tabi to Densetsu* as I went around

---

* *Mukashibanashi no Kenkyū.* Vol. I, 12 Nos. from May 1935 to April 1936; Vol. II, 12 Nos. from May 1936 to December 1937.—Tr's. note.

from island to island in the Ryūkyūs searching for oral tradition, particularly the folk tales.

To tell the truth, my first deep impression of even "Haibō-Tarō (Ash Boy)," a tale I had originally intended to discuss in this Introduction, was an example from Okierabujima. This should be thought of together with the Cinderella story in which a stepdaughter was always made to stay in front of the kitchen hearth. Young people of Japan like the beauty of the Cinderella tale, but they do not realize it is the same as "Komebukuro, Awabukuro" (the names of stepsisters in Japan). Even now people who know the famous work by our highly esteemed Miss Cox* are not aware that the same story was already contained in *Yūyō Zasso* of China in the eighth century.

I do not want merely to explain to people that such folk tales are the same. Instead, I want them to start with problems before their eyes and think about how it happens that in lands far apart the same tale appears, narrated in different languages. If one sets out to discuss this question with a foreigner, he will probably be told that one day when a missionary came to Japan he told it or some such explanation. As for me, I urge you to inquire patiently from old people nearby. But perhaps by now this old person's remarks have become too tedious for you.

Kunio Yanagita
April, 1960

---

* Marian Cox, "Cinderella," (PFLS XXVI). London, 1893.—Tr's note.

POSTSCRIPT

To the Japanese Edition

As Mr. Yanagita has already written at the opening of his Introduction, this book appeared for the first time thirty years ago in the Children's Library of Ars in 1930 as *Nippon no Mukashibanashi* (Japanese Folk Tales). Collection of tales had not progressed yet, making it difficult for him to select enough to make one volume. For that reason there were several among the tales that could not be called true folk tales. The principal purpose in publishing the present edition has been to eliminate those unsuitable ones and in their stead to supplement it with folk tales selected from material which has been gathered since that time. The results of this attempt are shown on the map at the beginning of the book.

We would like to explain the two conditions upon which we based our selection of the additional tales. The first is geographical. We wished to include even one tale from as many different regions as possible, but because good material is not well distributed, in some prefectures there are many tales collected and, to the contrary, some prefectures have had to be left blank. This is partly due to a reason which will be apparent later, but the main reason is that up till now collection has not been equal throughout the country. It is apparent on the map that in the prefectures of Aomori, Iwate, and Niigata there are many more tales than in the other neighboring prefectures. In these regions winters are long, the snow is deep, and there are many occasions to tell tales. That is why an abundance of tales have been preserved until recently and splendid scholars and collectors have appeared in those areas.

The second condition was based upon the idea of preparing this book for boys and girls of the upper elementary grades and junior high school. The contents of the tales and the way they are told are suitable for these young readers. It is usual to think that folk tales are mainly for children, but this is a recent development, for originally men, women, and old people would recite these or listen to them with pleasure. For this reason, it is natural that among folk tales there are many whose contents and impressions are not for children. Because we could not utilize such adult tales or those that are simple but coarse in this book, there was material which we have not used although plenty was available. The reason for the blank places on the map, then, was not only that tales were scarce, but because we could not find suitable ones in them.

Since these two conditions were the basis for selecting and writing tales from the extensive source material, we cannot say positively that each tale is the best example or form of the tale or that they have been selected as the most representative of Japanese folk tales. We have tried to choose those that were straight-forward and well arranged from as wide a distribution as possible.

At the end of each tale we have recorded the region and published the source, giving the editor's name for a book and for the magazine, the number and volume, but omitting the collector's name. When the source is a manuscript of an un-published collection, we have given the name of the collector and where it was collected. There are a number of humorous tales toward the end of the book which do not have the region of their origin, but such tales are found everywhere in the land and are not the kind we can pin down to one place.

In addition to these there are two or three taken from old books such as *Shasekishū* or *Seisuisho* or others that we have edited although our point of view may seem inconsistent. "Kobu Tori" (Getting a Tumor) and "Kurage Honenashi" (Why the Jellyfish Has No Bones) were transmitted as oral tales in various regions as well as being stories that are already set down in old books. We deliberately left them that way, thinking it would be of interest to the reader. When those old books were written, many such tales were told in the outskirts of the capital city and occasionally, depending upon the author, we can think they came to have a place in a record. The relationship of such old literary works to folk tales has been treated in careful detail by Mr. Yanagita in *Mukashibanashi to Bungaku* (Folk Tales and Literature).*

Finally, we wish to add a little to the explanation of the map. The stories from the early edition which have been retained and the newly added ones are given different signs in the distribution, but the numbering in this volume has been used to make it easy to locate them.

Hisako Maruyama
Yasuyo Ishiwara
April, 1960

---

* *Mukashibanashi to Bungaku*, Tokyo: Sōgensha, 1938.—Tr's. note.

REFERENCE INDEX

The numbers to the right refer to the number of the tale. Several tales have no reference while others have only a geographical reference. The former have been explained in the Postscript, the latter made from notations by Yanagita from information gained on his travels, in correspondence, or personal contacts. Yanagita's notation, though brief, is reliable.

12. Isogai, Isamu, *Akinokuni Mukashibanashi Shū* (Folk Tales of Aki, now Hiroshima) Tokyo: Oka Shoin, 1934 42

13. Iwakura, Toshio, *Kikaijima Mukashibanashi Shū* (Folk Tales of Kikai Island) Tokyo: Sanseidō (Zenkoku Kiroku), 1943 28-67

14. (same), *Koshikijima Mukashibanashi Shū* (Folk Tales of Koshiki Island) Tokyo: Sanseidō (Zenkoku Kiroku), 1944 81

15. (same) *Okinoerabu Mukashibanashi* (Folk Tales of Okierabu Island) Tokyo: Kokon Shoin, 1955 80

16. Iwasaki, Toshio, *Iwaki Mukashibanashi Shū* (Folk Tales of Iwaki) Tokyo: Sanseidō (Zenkoku Kiroku), 1942 .. 37-59

17. *Kaidōki,* Maki, 330, No. 130 (1223) (See an anthology of Japanese literature) 47

18. *Kanō Minzoku,* No. 4, 1952 (Kanō Folklore) Ishikawa 8

19. Katsurai, Kazuo, *Tosa Mukashibanashi Shū* (Folk Tales of Tosa) Kōchi: Kōchi Nippō-sha, 1948 36

20. *Kazuno Shi* (Records of Kazuno) Kemanai-machi, Kazuno-gun, Akita, 1877 43

21. Kikuchi, Isamu, *Ninohe Mukashibanashi Shū* (Folk Tales of Ninohe) Fukuoka-machi, Ninohe-gun, Iwate: 1947 .. 90

22. *Kyōdo Kenkyū* (Regional Studies),
 Vol. II, No. 6 (1914) 25
 (same) Vol. IV, No. 4 (1916) 6
 (same) Vol. IV, No. 7 (1917) 6
 (same) Vol. V, No. 4 (1931) 62

23. Makiguchi, Takeshi, *Shinano Mukashibanashi Shū* (Folk Tales of Shinano) Iida, Nagano: Yamamura Shoin, 1939 72

24. *Minamiazumi-gun Shi* (Records of Minamiazumi-gun) Toyoshina-machi, Minamiazumi-gun, Kyōikukai, 1923 .. 56

25. *Minkan Denshō* (Folklore), Vol. IV, No. 7 (1939) 40

26. *Minzoku* (Ethnos), Vol. I, No. 5 (1925) 11
 (same) Vol. I, No. 6 (1926) 17
 (same) Vol. III, No. 3 (1928) 18

27. Miyamoto, Tsuneichi, *Yoshino Saiō Minzoku Saihōki* (Notes on Gathering Folklore in Saiō, Yoshino) Tokyo: Nippon Shuppan Haikyū Kabushiki Kaisha, 1942 75

28. Mizusawa, Kenichi, *Tonto Mukashi Atta Gedo, Dai Isshū* (An opening formula, *Tonto Mukashi Atta Gedo*, Vol. 1) Tokyo: Miraisha, 1957 69-97

29. Moriguchi, Seiichi, *Kii Arita-gun Dōwa Shū* (Children's Stories of Arita-gun, Wakayama) Mimeographed by the author, 1916 12-60

30. *Mukashibanashi Kenkyū* (Study of Folk Tales),
    Vol. I, No. 2 (1935) 31
    (same) Vol. I, No. 7 (1935) 89
    (same) Vol. I, No. 8 (1935) 49
    (same) Vol. II, No. 3 (1936) 53

31. Mutō, Tetsushiro, *Akita Gunyū Gyotan* (Tales of Fishing Villages in Akita) Tokyo: Attic Museum, 1940 .. 41

32. Noda, Tayoko, *Tekkiri Anesama* (The Girl without Hands) Tokyo: Miraisha, 1958 65

33. Nomura, Denshi, *Ōsumi Kimotsuki-gun Hōgen Shū* (Dialect in Ōsumi, Kimotsuki-gun) Tokyo: Chūō Kōron-sha, 1942 8

34. Oda, Hideo, *Izawa-gun Mukashibanashi Shū* (Folk Tales of Izawa-gun) Iwate Nippō-sha, 1929 26

35. *Riyō Shū* (Folk Songs) Mombushō, 1914 45

36. Sasaki, Kizen, *Esashi-gun Mukashibanashi* (Folk Tales of Esashi-gun). Tokyo: Kyōdo Kenkyū-sha (Rōhen Sōsho), 1922 21-63-71

37. (same), *Rōō Yatan* (Nighttime Tales of an Old Woman) Tokyo, Kyōdo Kenkyū-sha, 1927 19-35-77-78-83-85

38. *Seisuisho* (1629) (See an anthology of Japanese literature) 70

39. *Shasekishū* Maki 5, Part One, No. 8 (1283) (See an anthology of Japanese literature) 2

40. *Shizuoka-ken Densetsu Mukashibanashi Shū* (Legends and Folk Tales of Shizuoka) Shizuoka-ken Joshishihan Gakko Kyōdo Kenkyūkai. Tokyo: Yajima Shoin, 1934 91

41. Sotoyama, Rekirō, *Echigo Sanjō Nangō Dan* (Tales of Southern Sanjō, Echigo, now Niigata) Tokyo: Kyōdo Kenkyū-sha (Rōhen Sōsho), 1922 13-15-27

COLLECTORS

1. Ikeda, Hiroko
2. Maruyama, Hisako
3. Osada, Sumako
4. Sato, Yoshihiro
5. Sugawara, Takiko

GEOGRAPHICAL INDEX

The number to the right refers to the number of the tale. For the benefit of those who are not familiar with the usual Japanese lists, which gives prefectures in a geographical order from the northeast to the southwest, this list has been made alphabetically.

MAP OF THE DISTRIBUTION OF THE TALES

From the Japanese Edition

Numbers are those of the stories. Those that are circled are newly selected tales; those without a circle are from the early collection.

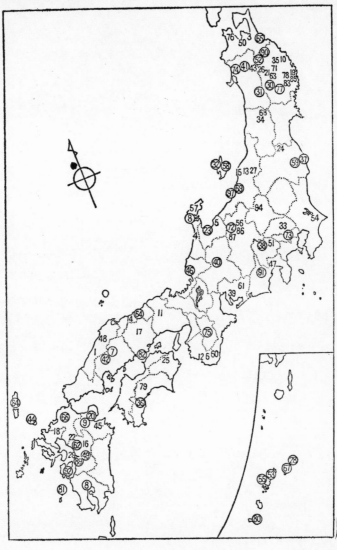

MAP OF THE DISTRIBUTION OF THE TALES

From the Japanese Edition